Facing Chemical Dependency In The Classroom

With Student Assistance Programs

ORVILLE A. DEAN

Health Communications, Inc.
Deerfield Beach, Florida

Orville A. Dean
Cleveland, Ohio

Library of Congress Cataloging-in-Publication Data

Dean, Orville A., 1950-
  Facing chemical dependency in the classroom with
student assistance programs.

  Bibliography: p.
  1. Student assistance programs — United States.
2. Drug abuse counseling — United States. 3. Personnel
service in education — United States. 4. School management
and organization — United States. I. Title.
LB3430.5.D42   1989   373.14'6   88-28411
ISBN 1-55874-004-X

©1989 Orville A. Dean
ISBN 1-55874-004-X

Published by: Health Communications, Inc.
            Enterprise Center
            3201 S.W. 15th Street
            Deerfield Beach, Florida 33442

Acknowledgments

I wish to thank . . .

Ted Sucher, Sandy Siebenschuh, Elsie Koncal, Paul Brickman, Julie Stough, Joe Chontos, Harriet Walker, Keli Keyes, Nell Taylor, Marty Webb, Emily Sanderson and Peter Rogers and the staff of Glenbeigh Hospital of Cleveland for their support and dedication in carrying the message of recovery.

Frank Barr, Barbara Terbanc and the Project CARE coordinators for their leadership in establishing student assistance programs.

The Faculty of the Gestalt Institute of Cleveland for their insight into systems and the healing process.

The workshop participants and clients who have shared part of their lives with me.

My family, friends and colleagues for their encouragement and support along the way.

Dedicated

with

Love and Gratitude

to

E. Leonard DeWitt

and the

DeWitt Family,

Ishpeming, Michigan

Contents

Tables & Figures

Prologue
The Dilemma

A History Of Alcoholism/Chemical Dependency

Chemical dependence is not a new illness. It has been with us forever. The term "chemical dependence" or "chemical dependency" replaced the older term "alcoholism" when the Baby Boom developed a wide array of dependencies besides alcoholism, but alcoholism remains our oldest and most pervasive chemical dependence. In this book chemical dependence will refer to preoccupation with, tolerance to and dependence on any legal or illegal mood-altering chemical. Alcohol is only one of the addicting drugs currently used by adolescents, along with marijuana, amphetamines, cocaine and heroin. Chemical use becomes dependence as the user continues despite obvious negative consequences in the user's emotional, family, occupational or social life.

Before World War I alcoholism/chemical dependence was seen as a moral problem to be treated by the church.

In fact, before F.D.R.'s social reforms, the church was practically the only social service agency in the United States and the only one to break the "no-talk" rule about alcoholism. The church used the only language it had to describe alcoholism — a language of morality. Spouses and children of alcoholics found refuge in strict fundamentalist churches in which abstinence from strong drink was the social norm.

During the 1920s in the U.S.A., alcoholism was viewed more as a legal problem than a moral issue and legislators assumed that strict behavioral measures, such as Prohibition, could illuminate the problem. Prohibition worked very well with non-alcoholic, law-abiding citizens, and drinking consumption was either eliminated or drastically reduced for most Americans. Prohibition did work for non-alcoholics. But for the alcoholic American who needed the chemical to function normally, Prohibition was circumvented to avoid the pain of withdrawal. Therefore a large demand created a network of organized crime to supply the illegal drug.

Prohibition of marijuana and cocaine in the 1980s seems to be repeating the story of the 1920s. Non-addicted, law-abiding U.S. citizens avoid cocaine and marijuana but chemical dependents, who need marijuana and cocaine to function normally, have created a demand which in turn has created an international network of suppliers.

After the Stock Market crash in 1929, the federal government could no longer afford to patrol the coastlines and break up the laboratories creating the illegal drug. And in 1933 the "Great Experiment" against ethyl alcohol was repealed.

During the 1930s scientific explanations began to replace religious answers to social problems. Ministers and priests were replaced by psychiatrists and psychologists who told us alcoholism was a secondary symptom of an underlying disorder. This theory maintained that if one could identify the painful childhood trauma or conflict, the alcoholic would be relieved of his psychic distress and *could return to social drinking*. Needless to say, many thousands of alcoholics spent millions of dollars to find the "underlying cause" and cure for their drinking problem. However, alcohol addicts could not get sober using this approach because they were looking at only part of the picture.

In the early 1930s Dr. William D. Silkworth, the Medical Director of Towns Hospital, developed the beginning of the modern disease theory of alcoholism. Silkworth stated that alcoholism involved a physical "allergy," which meant that the alcoholic responded differently physiologically than the non-alcoholic. This physiological difference produced abnormal drinking behavior. The "allergy" was permanent so that only abstinence would relieve the symptoms. Dr. Silkworth passed the idea on to one of his patients, Bill Wilson, who later helped co-found the fellowship and write the book of Alcoholics Anonymous.

Dr. Silkworth treated Bill, an alcoholic stockbroker, several times in the early 1930s. In the summer of 1934 Bill's wife, Lois, was told her husband would die unless he could remain abstinent. Bill continued his addiction to alcohol and sedatives and in November of 1934, an old prep school drinking buddy of his, who was temporarily sober, told Bill the steps he had used to find sobriety. Bill checked himself back into Towns Hospital under Dr. Silkworth's care and on December 14, 1934, Bill had a "spiritual experience" which released his desire to drink.

Bill began trying to sober up other alcoholics without success until Dr. Silkworth reminded him to stress the medical (physiological) side of the disease. With this advice in mind, Bill went to Akron, Ohio, on a business trip where he was confronted with the desire to drink. Instead of drinking, he made a call which connected him with another doctor, Dr. Robert Smith. Dr. Smith was also an alcoholic who was presently drinking. On May 12, 1935, Bill told Dr. Smith Dr. Silkworth's diagnosis of a physical allergy. Dr. Bob stopped drinking, relapsed at a doctors' convention, then took his last drink on June 10, 1935, to steady his hands before he performed an operation. Dr. Bob's last drink marks the founding of Alcoholics Anonymous.

Alcoholics Anonymous (AA) has always described alcoholism as a physical, emotional and spiritual disorder and has continued to use the definition which began in Dr. Silkworth's office — that alcoholism is a physical allergy coupled with a mental obsession. Alcoholics Anonymous was the first organization to recognize the physiological underpinning of the disease, which made drinking alcohol different for alcoholics and non-alcoholics. The beginning of the AA text book contains a letter from Silkworth called "The Doctor's Opinion," which describes his views of the allergic (or abnormal) physiological response. Because AA was the first organization to accurately define the disease, it has been the first to develop an effective treatment plan for it.

The Baby Boom, Schools And Chemical Dependency

The Big Book, the basic text of Alcoholics Anonymous, was published in 1939 and the fellowship began to grow in New York and Ohio during the Second World War. The servicemen who returned from the war a decade after the founding of AA began to produce the greatest surprise of demographic history. Between 1946 and 1956, 40 million children were born in the euphoria of a booming post-war capitalism. That first decade of the Baby Boom began to move through American society and disrupted every institution that it encountered. Schools, colleges, businesses and AA itself began to feel the impact of this demographic bulge as it travelled through American society.

Eighteen years after the Boom was born, it began to graduate from high school. These were the years of 1964 to 1974, the years of Lyndon Johnson and Richard

Nixon. These were exciting and hopeful, or frightening and disturbing years, depending on which side of the generation fence you stood. It was also the period in American history when alcoholism/chemical dependence began to invade our secondary school classrooms. Chemically dependent children began to become a normal part of every high school class.

Many who were not Baby Boomers prayed that adolescent chemical dependence would go away like Spiro Agnew, Vietnam and Watergate. Obviously it has not. It has become second generational. Alligators have replaced peace signs on kids' T-shirts, but the drug behavior remains the same.

After the Boom graduated from high school and college, it was termed the "Me Generation" of the 1970s. The Boom began to marry. Then in amazing numbers those marriages began to divorce. Between 1970 and 1979, the divorce rate in this country doubled. It increased 100% as the Baby Boom married and then unmarried. So the Boom became the most chemically dependent and most divorced generation in American history.

And what is this generation doing today? They are the parents of the 1980s and 1990s. Many parents of the 1980s were part of the drug culture of the 1960s. They are the most chemically dependent and most divorced generation in American history. And now they are raising the next generation of American citizens.

The Boom is also the most "enabling" generation as most Baby Boomers either used illegal drugs while young or had friends who used. Illegal drug use was common as the Boom came of age and generally no one intervened on their friends' use. After all, it was fun and a way of life during the college and service years.

In August of 1969 in New York State, near the town of Woodstock, half a million Baby Boomers gathered to celebrate their counter-culture with music and lots of drugs. During this music festival two babies were born. The two babies born at Woodstock were old enough to graduate from high school in June of 1987. So the children we are teaching in our high schools and treating in our treatment centers are the children of the Woodstock Nation — the children of the first Drug Culture.

Chemical dependency is not going away. It has become an ingrained part of American life. A generation ago, when educators or professional helpers wanted to learn about illegal drug use, they looked in a psychology text book under "Deviant or Abnormal Behavior." Today we know that statistically *not using mood-altering chemicals is deviant and abnormal behavior.* A generation ago it was generally considered socially acceptable to begin drinking and having sex only after you were 18 years old and married. In the 1960s using marijuana and having sex became a normal part of college life. During the 1970s drugs and sex moved back to high school where 14- to 17-year-olds began using drugs and having sex regularly. Now we know these behaviors have moved back to junior high school where many 11- to 13-year-olds are beginning to use drugs and sex regularly. Unfortunately 12-year-old children do not make good decisions about what they need to do to be part of the group.

Children grow up in a culture where the use of chemicals is expected and in some cases almost demanded. Any boy who watches a sports event on TV will know that drinking beer like the men in the commercials will make him more accepted and more virile. And any girl who sees an advertisement with a sexy woman and a bottle of liquor will learn that drinking makes her more acceptable and feminine. The two themes which American advertisers seem to spend the most money producing on primetime TV concern drugs and adultery. Any 12-year-old child can learn from this example that dealing drugs and cheating on your spouse are the two most exciting things adults do in America today — at least on TV.

So we live in a different kind of culture than we did when June and Ward were raising Beaver and Wally, and Ike and Jack were taking care of us and our most insidious peer pressure was staying up until 10 p.m. on a school night.

1

Dilemma Of
Chemical Dependency

The disease of chemical dependency — the preoccupation with, tolerance to and dependence on any legal or illegal mood-altering chemical — has plagued American society since colonial days. **Figure 1** depicts the progression of chemical use to chemical dependency or addiction.

History

Significant attitudes and events related to the history of chemical dependency in the United States are shown in Table 1.

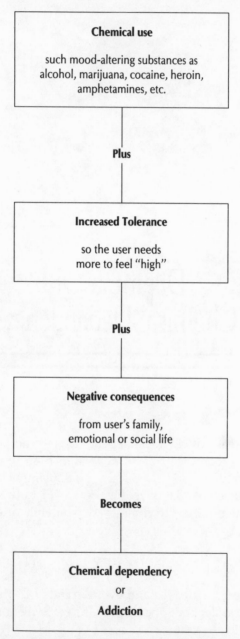

Figure 1. Progression of chemical use to chemical dependency

Table 1. Attitudes and events related to the history of chemical dependency in the United States

Years	Attitudes	Events
Before 1920	alcoholism seen as a moral problem	fundamentalist churches advocated abstinence
1920s	alcoholism viewed as a legal problem: *no talk* rule prevailed	Prohibition enacted by legislature; drinking eliminated or reduced by nonalcoholic, law-abiding citizens; demand of alcohol dependents created network of organized crime to supply alcohol illegally
1929		federal government no longer able to afford its attempts to enforce Prohibition
1930s	alcoholism perceived as physical, emotional and spiritual disorder	Dr. William Silkworth theorized alcoholism as a physical allergy coupled with a mental obsession
1933	*Great Experiment* considered a failure	Prohibition repealed
1934	hope for treatment of alcoholism through AA's self-help therapy	Bill W., recovering alcoholic, co-founded Alcoholics Anonymous (AA) based on Silkworth's theory
1939		*The Big Book*, basic text of AA published, contains an introduction by Dr. Silkworth
1940s	alcoholism experiences openly discussed and shared through self-help organization, AA	
1941-1945		AA grew, particularly in states of New York and Ohio
1946		birth of first of the "Baby Boom" generation, which moved through American society and disrupted every institution it encountered
1950s	environment nonpermissive; illegal drug use considered deviant and abnormal behavior	
1957		peak of "Baby Boom" generation

Years	Attitudes	Events
1960s	environment permissive for drug use and enabling*; alcohol/drug use and sex prevalent in colleges	toward end of decade educators noted high school students' scores on standardized tests were declining
1964		first of "Baby Boom" generation graduated from high school
1969	adolescent chemical dependency seen as part of a fad	Woodstock Music Festival celebrates the counter-culture with music and drugs
1970s	alcohol/drug use and sex prevalent in high schools; *Me* generation values of the "Baby Boom"	
1979	chemical dependency acknowledged as part of classroom culture; divorce rate nearly doubled	**Project CARE program founded in Ohio and headed by Dr. Frank Barr**
1980s	alcohol/drug use and sex prevalent in junior high schools; parents most chemically dependent and divorced generation in American history; statistically *not* using illegal drugs (including alcohol) considered deviant and abnormal behavior for adolescents	demand for mood-altering chemicals created illegal network of international suppliers; **Glenbeigh Hospital in Cleveland, Ohio, supported Project CARE concepts and began training teachers to work with chemically dependent adolescents**
	admitted awareness that genetic, neurological and metabolic factors make some more susceptible to addiction than others	Dr. James Milam published *Under the Influence* U.S. Dept. of Health published *Alcoholism: An Inherited Disease*
	breakthrough in knowledge of chemical dependencies promises new possibilities for treatment and prevention	National Institute of Alcoholism and Alcohol Abuse supporting genetic and physiological studies

Enabling: denying and making excuses for a problem; keeping a facade that everything is "okay."

Years	Attitudes	Events
1980s	children and grandchildren of alcoholics are recognized as the highest risk group for developing chemical dependency and other addictive diseases	Ackerman, Wegscheider-Cruse, Black, Subby and Woititz publish works on children of alcoholics and co-dependency
	HOPE for managing dilemma of chemical dependency in the classroom	intervention and support groups for chemical dependency continue to grow and spread throughout the nation

Chemically Dependent Students

Only within the last generation has chemical dependency become a special concern for teachers, school administrators, counselors and parents because it interferes with the academic, social and emotional development of school children. Statistics show that about 10 percent of any high school class in the United States, or two students per classroom, are beginning to exhibit some of the distracting symptoms of chemical dependency. (See Appendix for symptoms.)

Chemical dependency is a physical and emotional relationship with a mood-altering chemical which causes problems in the user's life. Chemical use becomes dependency as the user's body changes to tolerate more of the drug and the user continues using chemicals despite negative consequences in his or her emotional, family, academic, vocational or social life.

Illness develops when three elements are present: (1) a harmful or toxic agent; (2) a susceptible host and (3) a conducive environment. Chemical dependency develops through the interaction of addictive chemicals (toxic agent), genetic vulnerability (susceptible host) and family and cultural influences (conducive environment):

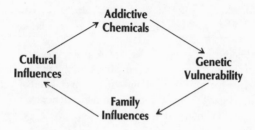

1. Addictive Chemicals

Chemicals vary in addictive potential from alcohol to heroin. In general the greater the euphoric experience, the more addictive the chemical. The three most abused chemicals in the classroom are alcohol, marijuana and cocaine. The reactions and consequences of these toxic chemicals are outlined in Table 2.

2. Genetic Vulnerability

Children do not all have an identical biochemical response when given the same dosage of the same drug. They have a variety of reactions. Current research indicates that the rate at which tolerance and dependence develop is strongly influenced by heredity. Children of alcoholics are four times more likely to develop chemical dependency than children from non-alcoholic families even when raised from birth apart from their biological parents. These studies demonstrate that not all children are at equal biogenetic risk for addiction.

3. Family Influences

Families range from very nurturing and supportive to very neglectful and abusive. Emotionally absent or unavailable parents provide an emotional void in which addictions can grow more easily. Characteristics which provide a conducive environment for addictions are families with:

1. Secrets — about addictions, abuse and affairs
2. Unexpressed Feelings — of anger, grief and shame

3. Other Compulsive Behaviors — such as work, food or sex

Families which keep secrets, don't express feelings and have work, food or sex addictions, are fertile ground for another generation of addictive behavior

4. Cultural Influences

Cultural and social pressure to use mood-altering chemicals surround children today. For many children their reference point for normal behavior is the media and their peer group, both of which provide ample permission and even pressure to use mood-altering chemicals. Table 3, based on a study by the National Institute on Drug Abuse, shows the extent of this cultural permission. The rate of use for high school seniors in America shows that not using any chemical has become statistically "deviant" and "abnormal" behavior and that American adolescents live in a conducive environment for developing chemical dependency.

Consequences of chemical dependency in adolescent students include:

1. Interrupted maturation
2. Unlearned problem-solving skills
3. Anguish
4. Augmentation

Interrupted Maturation

At best, the years between 14 and 24 are difficult for chemically free students from healthy families because major life decisions must be made, such as relating to parents, doing homework, falling in love, choosing a career, choosing a mate and developing a value system. In chemically dependent children (who are likely to be from dysfunctional families) whose first priority is to stabilize their system with a steady supply of addicting chemicals through a process called "partying," these major life decisions will become secondary and perhaps will not be attended to at all. Thus, emotional development will slow down, stop or even regress in these adolescents.

Table 2. Toxicity of the three most widely abused mood-altering chemicals by students in our nation's classrooms

Chemical	Reactions	Consequences
Alcohol (ethyl)	before body finally turns alcohol to acetate and eliminates it, alcohol is first converted to acetaldehyde, which *irritates* all cells, especially central nervous system and liver	perception, mood and ability to concentrate are affected
	evidence suggests if body is deficient in certain enzymes, the change from acetaldehyde to acetate occurs at slower rate, acetaldehyde accumulates in the brain, irritates nervous tissue and combines with brain amines to form isoquinlines, a substance similar to the opiates, explaining why some people are affected more than others by alcohol	body tolerates increasing amounts of alcohol and user has false sense of invulnerability to alcohol all bodily systems deteriorate, especially liver and central nervous system alcoholic experiences increased feelings of nervousness and irritability
	system craves more alcohol to alleviate stress of toxicity and withdrawal	brain chemistry may take months to heal into abstinence
Marijuana	mood-altering ingredient, THC (tetrahydrocannabinol), is fat soluble and half of amount consumed remains in body for 5-7 days after use (smoking twice a week means body is never chemically free). THC accumulates in brain impeding electrochemical flow, reducing energy in the brain and irritating nervous tissue	user feels elated with distorted sense of time and intensified experiences perception may be altered for months into abstinence

Chemical	Reactions	Consequences
Marijuana (cont.)	as THC is metabolized out of system, an imbalance is created, causing system to restabilize by craving more of the chemical	user experiences "amotivational syndrome" losing interest in work, school and family
		marijuana addict experiences increased feelings of nervousness and irritability
Cocaine	causes body to release such neurotransmitters as dopamine or serotonin into synapse between nerve cells	user may experience feelings of power and grandiosity followed by a physical and emotional crash
	the neurotransmitters stimulate receiving neurons and produce artificially induced electrochemical flow through the brain, resulting in rush of energy	brain is irritated after crash and user is unable to think clearly and experiences paranoia and depression
	after about 30 minutes a crash occurs because neurotransmitters are depleted	cocaine addict experiences increased feelings of nervousness and irritability
	body craves more drug to maintain feeling of normalcy	

Table 3. National Institute on Drug Abuse Survey of High School Seniors

	Class of												
	1975	1976	1977	1978	1979	1980	1981	1982	1983	1984	1985	1986	1987
Trends in 30-day prevalence: Percent who used in past month.*													
Heroin	0.4	0.2	0.3	0.3	0.2	0.2	0.2	0.2	0.3	0.3	0.3	0.2	0.2
Cocaine	1.9	2.0	2.9	3.9	5.7	5.2	5.8	5.0	4.9	5.8	6.7	6.2	4.3
Marijuana/Hashish	27.1	32.2	35.4	37.1	36.5	33.7	31.6	28.5	27.0	25.2	25.7	23.4	21.0
Alcohol	68.2	68.3	71.2	72.1	71.8	72.0	70.7	69.7	69.4	67.2	65.9	65.3	66.4
Trends in lifetime prevalence: Percent who ever used.													
Heroin	2.2	1.8	1.8	1.6	1.1	1.1	1.1	1.2	1.2	1.3	1.2	1.1	1.2
Cocaine	9.0	9.7	10.8	12.9	15.4	15.7	16.5	16.0	16.2	16.1	17.3	16.9	15.2
Marijuana/Hashish	47.3	52.8	56.4	59.2	60.4	60.3	59.5	58.7	57.0	54.9	54.2	50.9	50.2
Alcohol	90.4	91.9	92.5	93.1	93.0	93.2	92.6	93.8	92.6	92.6	92.2	91.3	92.2

*National Institute on Drug Abuse

Unlearned Problem-Solving Skills

Chemically dependent children will not learn the skills of problem solving either. Problems, such as homework, social skills, recreational skills or spiritual pursuits, take time to define, set goals, develop a plan, implement the plan and evaluate the outcome. Because the dependent students are preoccupied with putting a chemical back into their systems through "partying," they have not developed the needed problem-solving skills. Unfortunately a responsible adult, such as a parent, teacher or probation officer, must accept the responsibility that the students themselves cannot assume.

Anguish

Anguish or physical and emotional pain results from the accumulation of toxicity in the body of children using addictive chemicals. As acetaldehyde and THC build up and brain amines are depleted, the user begins to experience a feeling of psychic discomfort or distress. When nervous tissue is irritated by internal toxicity, the brain will perceive all incoming stimuli as irritating, and the user will report that he feels "nervous" and "irritated." Many well-meaning but naive helpers will try to change the user's environment, believing that will relieve the nervousness and irritability. Only long-term abstinence will relieve irritated nervous tissue due to heavy chemical use.

Augmentation

Augmentation occurs when an irritated brain changes, distorts or increases incoming stimuli so that the response seems inappropriate for the original stimulus. A diagram of this process would look like this:

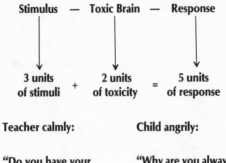

Teacher calmly: Child angrily:

"Do you have your   "Why are you always
homework ready?"   picking on me?"

A normal stimulus enters a toxic brain which produces an abnormal response. Because most people will respond with about the same emotional intensity as the preceding stimulus, the conversation quickly escalates to the point where both parties feel angry, hurt and misunderstood (Milam, 1974).

2

Chemically Dependent Systems: Schools And Classes

We live in a world where 10 percent of our high school students or about two children per classroom are exhibiting the symptoms of chemical dependency. In order to understand how chemical dependency impacts our schools it is necessary to know how a school operates as a system.

System theory tells us that a system is comprised of an organized collection of parts and that the whole is greater than the sum of its parts. If any part of a system is changed, the entire system will be out of balance and will have to develop a new homeostasis or a new balance.

A school is a collection of students, teachers, disciplines, departments, classrooms and buildings. And each school and each classroom has developed its own homeostasis, equilibrium or state of balance. Each school building and each classroom within the building has developed its own feeling, tone, atmosphere, overt and covert rules and bases of power within administration, faculty and students.

When none of the students are physiologically or emotionally impaired, the system works well. Information is passed from one generation to the next in an atmosphere of trust, safety and respect. But when chemical dependency invades the system, something happens. When 10 percent of the student body are toxic from the drug they used the day before, the old system begins to break down and a new homeostasis is created — a homeostasis which allows the system to function as efficiently as possible with chemical dependency present in the system. This is a little bit like learning to walk with a stone in your shoe. You can't walk with the same poise or run with the same speed but at least you can still move and besides it doesn't hurt that much if you try not to think about it.

Symptoms of Chemical Dependency In Schools

All systems respond to prolonged exposure to toxic chemicals: cells, tissue, organs, families, classes, school systems and communities. A school system which has been impacted by chemical dependency usually shows four characteristics: increased student unmanageability, decreased student learning, increased teacher burnout and increased administrative effort. (See Figure 2, page 32.)

Increased Student Unmanageability

Toxicity from intoxicating mood-altering chemicals remains in the system for several days and irritates the brain cells. A toxic student's central nervous system cannot manage itself nor can anyone else manage the moods of a toxic brain. Student unmanageability may take the form of overt acting out, disrespect, violence, abuse or truancy or it may take a more passive form, such as drowsiness, apathy, isolation, unfinished assignments and disrespect.

Decreased Student Learning

Toxic central nervous systems cannot learn as well as nontoxic ones. The first priority for an irritated neuron is to find relief from its distress. The first priority of an irritated child is to find relief, not the academic subject being taught. Toxic brains find it hard to focus on the causes of the War of 1812 or gerund phrases. Toxic brains also tend to be disruptive and if a teacher spends five minutes per 50 minutes of a classroom period managing the unmanageable kids, the amount of education that can possibly take place has been decreased by 10 percent. That means the other kids in the class will learn 10 percent less material that day, that month, that year and this decline will be reflected in standardized test scores.

Increased Teacher Burnout

Teachers who interact with two toxic brains per class each day become tired. A teacher with five academic classes must try to manage about ten sets of irritated brains each day, not counting the toxic kids at lunch, on the playground and in the halls. Children of alcoholics, spouses of alcoholics and teachers of alcoholics become exhausted trying to control the uncontrollable and manage the unmanageable. Children, spouses and teachers of alcoholic/chemical dependents suffer a predictable emotional response to living or working with an irritated toxic brain.

Increased Administrative Effort

Administrators spend much of their time trying to manage the chemically dependent student and the children of alcoholics who are acting out their emotional or physiologic distress. Assistant principals in charge of discipline spend the majority of their time trying to manage the unmanageable students and listening to the complaints of irate students, teachers and parents. Guidance counselors and school psychologists spend a disproportionate amount of time working with children and friends of alcoholics/chemical dependents who are traumatized by an intimate relationship with an addict.

The Chemically Dependent Class

If the only child in the class that was influenced by chemical dependency was the dependent child, we might be able to ignore it.

However *every child's attitude, mood and behavior influences every other child's attitude, mood and behavior.* If part of a system changes, the whole system will change. When two or three students begin to react to a friend's toxic behavior, they develop a condition chemical dependency counselors have called co-dependence or co-dependency. Co-dependency is an emotional syndrome associated with family and friends of chemical dependents, who get caught up in the emotional roller coaster of the disease and unwittingly help the disease continue through their own denial and enabling. Co-dependent students begin to experience unpredictable behavior, emotional mood swings, change of attitude and values, and increasing dishonesty. Therefore, the co-dependent friends of toxic students become emotionally unmanageable also.

A class with actively chemically dependent students feels like a chemically dependent family: tense, unpredictable and confusing. Everyone wonders what's going to happen next. What crisis will erupt today? Teachers teach in between crises which are never really resolved — the more crises management necessary, the less education occurs.

The atmosphere of tension, unpredictability and fear which pervades the alcoholic home begins to settle in the chemically dependent class and influences all the children in the class. When class feels scary and unpredictable, some students will use the defenses of children in an alcoholic home. The responsible students will become more responsible and rigid, the quiet child will become quieter to avoid conflict, the clown will tell more inappropriate jokes to break the tension and the rebel will act out the emotional pain of the class.

Education in this class will happen when the teacher isn't preoccupied with the chemically dependent and co-dependent students and when the other children feel relaxed enough to concentrate on the subject. *If a teacher has to spend five minutes per 50-minute classroom period managing the unmanageable student, there will be a 10 percent drop in the amount of education that can possibly take place during that class period.* That means potentially 10 percent less education per class, per day, per month, per year and per high school education.

3

Teaching With Chemical Dependency In The Classroom

Children, spouses and teachers of chemically dependent persons are in an intimate working relationship with someone whose moods and behavior are unpredictable and potentially hurtful. The chemically dependent system, whether family or class, is stressful and all members of the system will begin to adapt new behaviors to protect themselves.

Children, spouses and teachers of chemically dependent people will travel through four predictable stages in their relationship with the disease.

1. They will deny the presence of the disease or any dysfunction in the system.
2. They will attempt to control the person who appears to be the most symptomatic.

3. They will become angry because organic toxicity and emotional pain does not respond well to external controls.

4. They will begin to experience a crippling feeling of fear, self-doubt and shame, which they will not talk about. This final stage of the relationship is called burnout or late stage co-dependency.

Denial

Children, spouses and teachers of alcoholics and addicts deny the presence of the disease for a number of reasons. Probably the most obvious is that they really don't know what is causing this strange behavior since most people have no formal training about alcoholism or chemical dependency.

Spouses fear they may have caused their partner's increased drinking because they were not smart enough, pretty enough or rich enough. Children of alcoholic or abusive parents do not understand what is causing their parents' behavior so they assume they caused it. Spouses and children of dysfunctional partners and parents don't talk about the family secret. They feel the family shame and they protect the family self-esteem by denying the presence of addiction or abuse.

A motive for denial in the class involves the teacher's attempt to protect his or her own self-esteem. Most people believe that good teaching by a good teacher will promote a healthy classroom atmosphere and motivate students to learn. This belief is true when chemical dependency is not present in the classroom. But if little Johnny (who is drinking wine after school) cannot sit still at his desk and if little Suzy (who is smoking pot in the evening) doesn't turn her homework in on time, then who is held accountable? The burden of responsibility falls on the teacher.

Tradition suggests that if the teacher was just more interesting, dynamic, relevant and intelligent, then these kind of academic and classroom management problems wouldn't occur.

Countless stories in the media recount the woes in modern education: poor standardized test scores, illiterate seniors and student violence. Unfortunately the culprit in many of these stories seems to be, as usual, the co-dependent person — the teacher.

If these are some of the prevailing cultural beliefs, then what teacher is going to admit she has problems in class? For many educators it seems safer to smile bravely and pretend everything is really "fine" rather than look at the enormity of the dilemma.

The ability to work with toxic children has become an important part of any high school teacher's job expectations and denial is one of the ways teachers maintain their professional self-esteem.

Control

Denial never makes the problem go away so usually the next stage for children, spouses and teachers of chemical dependents is to try to control the objectionable behavior. Trying to control chemically dependent behavior is an attempt to restabilize the system. It is an effort on the part of children, spouses and teachers of alcoholics to create order, predictability and security.

Spouses try to control their alcoholic, abusive or neglectful partners through a variety of techniques such as throwing out the liquor, losing weight or threatening to leave. Children learn to control their alcoholic, abusive or neglectful parents by being super-responsible and mature or self-destructive and immature. Many of the super-responsible children grow up and become teachers or other professional helpers and get paid for using the defense mechanisms they learned as children.

Children and spouses slowly become tired of trying to manage toxic brains. So do teachers. Teachers have been managing unruly students for centuries and in the past have been fairly successful with most students. But the chemically dependent student is a new kind. The student with an irritated, toxic nervous system defies traditional classroom management methods.

When classroom teachers try to manage their acting-out students, they tend to revert to classroom management techniques they learned in college. One of these is developing the ideal seating chart.

Developing the ideal seating chart involves dividing up the unmanageable children into different areas of the classroom. Separating toxic kids theoretically reduces their potential combustibility when they sit together. So a teacher may line up all the "druggies" on opposite sides of her class. This seems to work for a while until they begin to lob things across the room.

Another method may be to line up all of the acting-out students in the front row because if we are physically close to children and can put our hands on them in a supportive, nurturing way, then they feel loved and warm and they don't act out.

Well, this may work for a while until the teacher turns around to write on the blackboard and the toxic kids lose control again. Seating charts cannot control neurologic and emotional distress and its consequent behaviors.

When seating charts don't work, teachers may try to develop the perfect lesson plan as a way of controlling student behavior. The idea is that by creating a sufficiently stimulating, exciting and creative lesson plan the teacher will be able to seduce the unmanageable child into the orbit of the lesson plan and the child will not act out. Something with enough stimuli in it so that it will engage even the most confused and distractable mind is best. So the teacher stays up to 12:00 or 1:00 a.m. Sunday evening writing the perfect lesson plan. And who is she writing the lesson plan for? The unmanageable kids, because first you have to manage the unmanageable students before you can teach the teachable students. When a teacher spends her weekend trying to figure out a lesson plan or seating chart that will control her toxic or unmanageable students so she can get through 50 minutes without being insulted or humiliated again, she is being controlled by these children. The toxic or unmanageable kids are controlling the class and she is reacting by trying to put out brush fires and do a little teaching in between.

Anger

Controlling toxic behavior never works, so the next stage to which children, spouses and teachers of chemical dependents move is the anger stage. This stage of the relationship is characterized by resentment and distrust on all sides. Co-dependents are angry at the chemical dependents for disrupting their lives. And the chemical dependents are angry at the co-dependents for trying to control their behavior.

Spouses become angry at their alcoholic, abusive or neglectful partners but are usually afraid of expressing it directly so they repress their feelings and develop stress-related illness such as headaches, ulcers and colitis. Children of alcoholic, abusive or neglectful parents do not feel safe sharing their anger with a parent so they carry their anger to school and blow up at the shop teacher who reminds them of their father.

How is anger managed in a chemically dependent class? It is usually repressed or displaced just as in a chemically dependent family. Anger becomes an obvious but unstated feeling of the classroom. The toxic students are irritated at the teacher who attempts to control their behavior, and the teacher becomes angry as the toxic students continue to interfere with attempts to teach them. Often an underground guerrilla war begins to emerge in the classroom with the "drunks" angry at the teacher and the teacher angry at the "drunks." And the harder the teacher tries to control the uncontrolled kids, the more they try to sabotage the lesson plans. Usually this war remains a covert action between students and teacher, trying to control or harass one another, and rarely talking directly about the process. Even if the war is identified, almost never is the disease of chemical dependency and its toxic consequences mentioned.

What kind of learning experience does this provide for the whole class? Most kids will remember the process of the class longer than the content. Teachers are paid to transmit the content of various disciplines to their students. The process involves all the thousands of bits of nonverbal communication, feelings and social interactions which occur during the 50-minute class. Often a student will have very little recall of the content, such as what years we fought the Civil War, but will have excellent recall of the social interactions of the class.

For instance, when little Johnny comes home from school, his mother may ask him what he learned in school today. He may not have any idea of the content that was presented but is very clear on the process. And he may reply, "It was great. Mrs. Jones asked for the homework assignment. George told her to drop dead and then everyone laughed. Mrs. Jones turned bright red and began to yell at George. Then she told us to put our heads down on the desk for the rest of the period while she took George to the Assistant Principal. It was great, Mom. We didn't learn anything."

Children remember the process better than the content and if the process is infected with the insidious covert anger of chemical dependency, the experience will not teach what is in the written curriculum. It will teach the class how to live around chemical dependence and co-dependence. The presence of chemical dependence in the classroom becomes like the *"elephant in the classroom."* Everyone on some level knows it's there, but no one knows exactly how to address it. The class and teacher then become preoccupied with the symptoms without addressing the source.

Sometimes teachers like to believe they are so professional (controlled) that other people don't know how upset they really feel. This, however, is a myth.

Controlled feelings are felt by others as controlled feelings. Every day most teachers have over 100 students staring at their bodies from head to toe. Students know how their teachers look better than the teachers do. After all, if you spend 50 minutes a day, five days a week, four weeks a month staring at someone's body, you will get to know it well. Students know every pair of shoes their teachers own. And they know that when they see the vein in a neck bulge, a face turn red, eyes get big, breathing get heavy, and when they see the muscle in a jaw start to twitch, they know they've got their teacher. They know they've won.

What does the teacher do with the energy of that anger? The natural response to a threatening stimulus is fight or flight, but screaming at a student or running out of a classroom crying is inappropriate. So the energy of that anger is repressed and frozen in the body where it may erupt later as stress-related medical problems. Stress-induced somatic complaints are not uncommon for teachers who work with toxic kids. Some of the energy which is not frozen into the body may be displaced and carried back into the teacher's own family, where the family will have to deal with the anger which was repressed in the classroom. It is sometimes difficult for a teacher of a chemically dependent class to focus her full attention on her family if she is still preoccupied with the unresolved conflicts back at school.

Co-dependent Burnout

Chemical dependency affects entire systems, not just individuals. Children, spouses and teachers of chemical dependents respond in a predictable progressive series of emotional reactions and defensive strategies. They travel through denial, control strategies, repressed anger and finally sink into feelings of fear and self-doubt. This journey has been given different names by different observers. Educational theorists call this process "burnout" and often recommend workshops in "stress management." Professionals in the field of chemical dependency look at this same set of data and call it late stage co-dependency. Whatever label one applies to this phenomenon, the feelings associated with the condition are the same: fear, shame and self-doubt.

Many spouses in alcoholic marriages wake up dreading the future and think, "I don't want to be married to that person anymore; I don't want to be insulted and hurt anymore. But I can't afford to leave financially. I have to stay."

How do teachers of chemical dependents feel as they prepare for another day of managing their toxic charges? Many become afraid of being hurt again and think, "I don't want to go back into that classroom today. I don't want to be insulted and humiliated anymore. I don't want to be hurt again today, but I can't afford to leave. I have no other job. I have to stay." And if a teacher continues teaching because she can't afford to leave, the kids know it, and the whole classroom system is affected.

The most painful legacy of co-dependence is that people begin to believe what the chemically dependent person says about them. Children, spouses and teachers of alcoholics or chemical dependents begin to believe what a toxic brain tells them. Remember an irritated brain experiences all incoming stimuli as irritating, so children, spouses and teachers are perceived as sources of irritation. The toxic brain believes if only the child, spouse or teacher would change their behavior, the irritation would stop. So addicts report through continuous verbal and nonverbal statements that children, spouses or teachers are irritating them when, in fact, the source of irritation is in their central nervous system, not in their environment.

Children in a chemically dependent family, for instance, listen to a toxic parent insult them and begin to believe what they hear. Such children may think to themselves, "My momma says I'm stupid. Momma knows me better than anyone. I guess I'm stupid."

What do teachers hear from their chemically dependent students? They hear nonverbal and verbal messages of toxic nervous tissue. These messages are sent through children's facial expressions, bored sighs, graffiti on the desks, notes left behind in class, shouts in the playground and overheard conversations in the hall. The message they hear is, "This class is boring; this homework is stupid; you are boring; you are stupid; you are inadequate. I hate this class and I hate you! You are no good!"

And the tragedy is that if teachers hear this message every day, every month and every year, some teachers begin to believe it and they begin to experience the pain of self-doubt. Some teachers begin to say to themselves something like, "Maybe the kids are right. Maybe it is my fault. Maybe I just wasn't cut out to be a teacher. My father was a teacher and he never had the kinds of behavior problems in class that I do. I guess it must be me. It must be my fault. Maybe I should find another career where I can do a better job. But I have no other skills; I have to stay."

The pain of a teacher's co-dependence and self-doubt is felt more acutely because the slings and arrows of toxic brains are thrown not at the teacher's lesson plans or test procedure, but at the teacher's character and personality. The messages say not that the teaching behavior is bad, but that the teacher's being, the total person, is bad. Criticism of a teacher's behavior or methods may produce the feeling of guilt with a desire to change the behavior to alleviate the guilt. Criticism of a teacher's character or personality may result in the feeling of shame with a desire to withdraw or retaliate to protect the self from further shame-inducing attacks.

Who can a teacher talk to about these feelings? Most teachers do not want to talk with their professional colleagues about their feelings for fear that others may not have similar feelings, which would only compound the feeling of inadequacy. Teachers usually do not want to tell the administration about these feelings for fear of being perceived as incompetent, and no one can afford

that perception when budgets are being cut. Most
teachers have stopped telling their spouse about painful
feelings related to work for fear of having the spouse
recommend changing careers.

**So what happens to their feelings of inadequacy and
pain, which result from teaching a chemically dependent
class?** Some good teachers quit to find other jobs but they
carry the same feeling of running away from failure as
the spouse who walks out of an alcoholic marriage or the
child who escapes from alcoholic parents. Other teachers
develop defending strategies to protect themselves from
their potentially shame-inducing environment. Rigidity,
perfectionism, contempt and withdrawal are strategies
often used by co-dependent teachers, spouses and
children to protect themselves from further feelings of
inadequacy and shame.

These defensive strategies of rigidity, perfectionism,
contempt and withdrawal protect co-dependent teachers'
self-esteem and temporarily reduce teachers' personal
stress levels. Unfortunately, these strategies tend to
increase the stress levels in the class as the school year
progresses. In their attempt to manage the students and
their own emotions, they may become rigid, controlling
and so "rule oriented" that they lose the ability to be
creative, spontaneous and warm. Teachers may avoid
feelings of inadequacy in themselves by becoming
increasingly perfectionistic and demanding of themselves
and their students. They may become increasingly
contemptuous of their students, engaging in endless
gossip and blame sessions with other faculty rather than
talking about their own feelings of confusion and hurt.
And some teachers distance themselves from their
painful unacceptable feelings of sadness and self-doubt,
and emotionally withdraw from their students to avoid
any more shame-inducing transactions.

These defending strategies which protect the teacher
are experienced by the entire class as another set of
stressors. The teachers' rigidity, perfectionism, contempt and withdrawal are painful and confusing to the

students and the message communicated to the whole class is that the whole class is bad and unlovable. The defending strategies developed in response to a minority of students is felt by all the students. The nontoxic students interpret the teacher's defenses as a response to *their* inherent "badness," while the toxic kids use the defenses as yet another source of irritation, hence another excuse to act out.

The feelings of anxiety, guilt, anger, fear and shame, which are part of a chemically dependent classroom, are not experienced by all people with equal intensity. People raised in a chemically dependent or dysfunctional family will have a different experience in an unpredictable or abusive environment than someone raised in a healthy functional family. Teachers from dysfunctional homes and teachers from healthy families will respond differently to a chemically dependent classroom.

Teachers who come from healthy family systems may be shocked at the behavior and language of a chemically dependent/co-dependent class. However, these teachers, having had 18 years' worth of healthy relationships on which to base their self-esteem and sense of reality are able to view the situation with some objectivity and detachment. As the years wear on, some of these teachers are able to maintain the sense of personal integrity they developed as children by holding students responsible for their behavior, detaching from the toxic comments and keeping the lines of communication open with supervisors, colleagues, parents and students. But some teachers begin to lose their sense of worth as they lose control of their environment.

Teachers who came from alcoholic, painful or dysfunctional homes have more difficulty in a dysfunctional classroom. Having spent their first 18 years in an unpredictable painful system, they learned to accept the blame for their painful family. After all, didn't their parents (the alcoholic and co-dependent) tell them they were at fault? If only they had kept their room cleaner, Mom would not have been so depressed, and if only they had made the varsity, Dad would not have gotten drunk and would have spent more time at home. They assumed as children it was all their fault.

When a person with this kind of personal history becomes a teacher and enters a stressful classroom, all the old feelings return — feelings of inadequacy, fear and shame and the old defending strategies to protect themselves, such as rigidity, perfectionism, contempt and withdrawal. Adult children of alcoholics who teach in chemically dependent classes need to learn about co-dependency and develop strategies to cope with chemical dependency in their classes.

Increased Efforts By Administrators, Guidance Counselors And Special Education Teachers

Administrators have become preoccupied with the symptoms of chemical dependency, such as truancy, vandalism, acting out in class, theft and student violence. Parents and society want to know what the schools are going to do about children who are interrupting other students' learning. The subpopulation of students who regularly use chemicals and "acting-out" children of alcoholics take up most of the assistant principal's time.

The typical response to the unmanageable student has been some form of in-school or out-of-school suspension. This behavioral approach may be effective with children whose perceptions are not clouded with drugs, but for the toxic child in or out-of-school suspension will have no effect on the child's behavior. Many children in in-school suspension rooms are regularly involved with drug and alcohol use. Often these kids were high when they committed their offense or were coming off of being high or planning on getting high soon. In-school suspension will not change their drug-use pattern if they are chemically dependent.

Assistant principals and in-school suspension and later the police and prison systems have been the primary means by which society has managed our unmanageable chemical dependents. Continuing to use this system does not address the illness underlying the unmanageable behavior and it offers no solution for the system or the chemically dependent person.

Administrators and teachers are not the only school personnel preoccupied with the symptoms of chemically dependent children or the children of alcoholic parents. **Guidance counselors,** when not rearranging schedules, spend most of their time in crisis counseling with (a) chemically dependent children who are in trouble academically or socially, (b) children of alcoholics, whose home life is interfering with their ability to concentrate or develop socially and (c) friends of chemical dependents who are preoccupied with their boyfriend's or girlfriend's unpredictable behavior.

Guidance counselors also spend time working with children on issues such as dropping out, unplanned pregnancies and suicide. Chemically dependent children and children of alcoholics are the highest risk group for dropping out, getting pregnant and planning suicide. Children preoccupied with their own use or a parent's use of chemicals can't concentrate on school so they drop out, they feel disconnected so they become sexually active. They feel hopeless so they plan their own death. Guidance counselors spend most of their counseling time working with symptoms of chemical dependency or co-dependency.

Special education teachers are also preoccupied with chemically dependent children and children of alcoholics. Many children, who are in special education classes are also using chemicals heavily and have difficulty focusing on assignments at school. Some children find themselves so preoccupied, depressed, anxious or numb from living in painful chaotic homes with alcoholic parents that they can't stay up with the mainstream students. So the special education teacher is another professional dealing with more aspects of unidentified chemical dependency and co-dependency.

Without training in the symptoms of chemical dependency and co-dependency, classroom teachers, assistant principals, guidance counselors and special education teachers will continue trying to manage symptoms of an unnamed insidious illness. Time and energy which is going into trying to control toxic or co-dependent behavior is not used helping the other children with their academic, social and emotional growth.

Many classroom teachers, guidance counselors, learning disability specialists and school administrators have realized that identifying and treating the source of the dysfunction is more efficient than treating the symptoms of the illness forever.

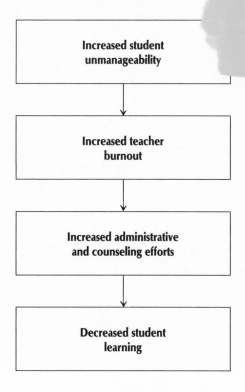

Figure 2. Four clues to existence of chemical dependency in the classroom

4

Solving A Problem
Versus Managing A Dilemma

Whether school boards and administrators decide to deal with chemical dependency in the classroom on a short-term or long-term basis depends on whether they believe they are facing a problem or a dilemma. Problems have a limited number of variables and can be solved. Dilemmas, such as inflation, pollution, race relations, poverty, nuclear waste, population explosion or chemical dependency, have a larger number of variables and cannot be solved. However, dilemmas like these can be managed, and must be, if we are to survive.

Learning disability is an example of a dilemma to be managed, not a problem to be solved. Learning disabilities cannot be solved, but they can and have been managed more effectively. In the past if a child didn't learn, he was considered either "stupid" or "lazy" and that was that. Some people began to wonder about these diagnoses and began to obtain more training. They realized some children had neurological, emotional and behavioral problems that prevented them from learning like other children. These teachers returned to schools and established special programs for the learning-disabled child. At first these programs were seen as unnecessary frills, but gradually they came to be accepted as an important aspect of a school's educational services. Learning disabilities were not solved, but they began to be managed more effectively.

The history of chemical dependency is similar to that of learning disabilities. Some teachers, wondering about the diagnosis of "bad" kids or "lazy" kids, started seeking further training. They discovered that many children are either chemically dependent or children of alcoholics, and, as a result, have difficulty concentrating and studying. These teachers returned to school and began to set up programs for chemically dependent children as well as for co-dependent children of alcoholics or other troubled families. At first viewed as unnecessary, these services gradually have become an important part of the total pupil services in the schools of the 1980s and 1990s.

Chemical dependency is not a problem to be solved and eliminated but a dilemma to be managed day by day. When people talk about solving the drug problem, they can experience disappointment when they find it can't be solved and then tend to become discouraged and quit. We will not solve the dilemma of chemical dependency, but we can manage it effectively.

5

Managing The Dilemma Of Chemical Dependency In School

Student Assistance Programs

Many classroom teachers, guidance counselors, learning disability specialists, school administrators and parents have realized that identifying and treating the source of the dysfunction in their chemically dependent students are more efficient than forever treating the symptoms of the illness. One means of dealing with this source of dysfunction is using student assistance programs similar to employee assistance programs developed by business and industry to work with troubled workers. These programs identify workers on the basis of declining job performance and then refer them for specialized help in the community. This procedure has proven more humane and cost effective than ignoring the problem or terminating valued employees.

Schools have begun to adopt the same principles.
Student assistance programs are emerging throughout
the United States as administrators and school boards,
like their counterparts in business, also recognize the
program as being humane, cost effective and beneficial
to both students and staff.

Project CARE

One student assistance program that has worked
successfully in over 100 school districts in northeast
Ohio is Project CARE. Since its beginning in 1979, the
program has dealt effectively with the illness of chemical
dependency and co-dependency in the classroom.

In the fall of 1979 at the Greater Cleveland School
Superintendents Association, educators acknowledged
that student alcohol and drug use was undermining the
quality of student education and faculty morale. They
issued a statement of concern about drugs and alcohol,
and suggested a response which included promoting
public awareness, teacher education and student prevention, as well as supporting treatment and rehabilitation.
This call to action resulted in the establishment of
Project CARE as the organizing force that would
implement the superintendents' ideas.

Project CARE was given an office in a local school
board building, and two staff began coordinating
services. Dr. Frank Barr, a retired school superintendent,
was named executive director. It was decided that a
school administrator would have more influence on
other school administrators than would a professional
counselor for alcohol/drug abuse. Assisted by Barb
Tarbanc, Project CARE's dedicated managing director,
Dr. Barr began to carry a message of recovery to the
families and schools in their area.

6

The Student Assistance
Program Model

The basic formula for implementing a student assistance program that focuses on chemical dependency
includes:

1. Written school policy
2. Trained school personnel
3. Core Teams and a Student Assistance Program
   Coordinator
4. Behavioral observation forms and referral
   process
5. School curriculum and support groups

School Policy

Experience has shown that chemical dependency programs in the school need to be supported by the school board with a written policy. This policy supports and validates the establishment of chemical dependency/ student assistance programs, as well as issuing warning to the community that the illegal use of addictive chemicals will not be ignored.

This policy should also declare that:

1. The school is committed to students reaching their full potential.
2. Alcoholism/chemical dependency is a progressive, chronic illness, which can and does affect adolescents in achieving their potential.
3. Student assistance programs focusing on prevention and intervention of chemical abuse and dependence are necessary to help students develop their full potential.

(See Appendix for a sample of School Board Policy on Student Drug/Alcohol Abuse, for a Sample School Board Policy on Chemical Dependency for School Employees, and for a Sample Administrative Regulation on Procedure for Handling Instances of Possession, Sale, Distribution or Use of Drugs or Alcohol by Students.)

These student assistance programs must be a priority of any school system because chemically dependent children are unable to function appropriately in the classroom or school community. An effective program will focus on three areas:

1. **Prevention** — averting school children from taking their first drink or drugs while they are in school
2. **Intervention** — interceding when alcohol or drugs begin to interfere with the lives of children
3. **Support services** — preventing the relapse of children into active chemical dependency

Board policy must support the establishment of:

1. Prevention education and curriculum at the elementary school level
2. A system at the secondary school level to implement drug and alcohol services for abusing children, addicted children, as well as children who are in emotional distress because of a close friend's or family member's use (co-dependency)

This system may require a full-time, paid chemical dependency coordinator or student assistance program coordinator.

Staff Training

In order to help children who are being affected by addictive chemicals, teachers, guidance counselors and administrators need training. Much of the reliable physiological and psychological research on addiction and children of alcoholics has been published since 1970. The majority of our academic department heads and administrators received their training in education before 1970 when accurate addiction information was unavailable. Although an abundance of information is accessible today, very few liberal arts colleges or colleges of education have courses to train teachers to work effectively with abusing/addicted children or with children from homes having abusing/addicted members.

Therefore, the majority of teachers coming into our nation's classroom have had no formal training to deal with:

1. Ten percent of children in their classrooms who are abusing or addicted to mood-altering chemicals or
2. The other ten percent who are reacting to a friend's or parent's chemical dependency

This 20 percent, or one out of five students, may consume the majority of teachers' attention and time. The unmanageable 20 percent may cause 80 percent of teachers' classroom management worries. Yet, with no formal training to deal effectively with this minority, teachers will waste valuable class time groping for a strategy. Training teachers to recognize and work with abusing/addicted and co-dependent children will allow more efficient use of class time.

In terms of the Gestalt theory (which states that we can only pay attention to one thing at a time, and that something in our awareness is figural and the rest is background), training in chemical dependency helps teachers discern the figural and background aspects of their classrooms. In the case of chemical dependency in children, teachers can view:

1. Student behavior problems (either acting out or passive behavior) as figural, with alcohol/drug use as part of the background (see Figure 3A) or
2. Student alcohol/drug use as figural, with problems or passive behavior as part of the normal background (see Figure 3B)

If teachers see the symptoms of chemical use as figural, they can begin to see how toxicity influences grades, behavior and peer group relations.

If children have stronger emotional relationships to chemicals than to their parents, teachers or values, then that relationship needs to be identified and addressed. Training teachers, guidance counselors and administrators in identifying signs and symptoms of alcohol/drug use helps make this relationship figural so that it can be addressed as a primary issue affecting all areas of students' lives.

Training programs and workshops in chemical dependency have been established throughout the United States and are conducted most often by chemical dependency treatment centers having expertise in this field. The most effective type of training program is the

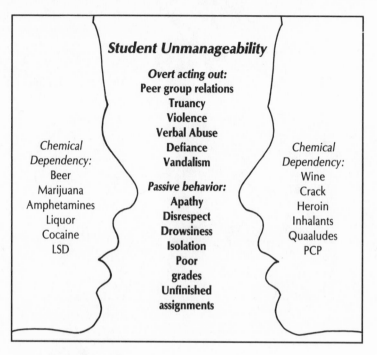

Figure 3(A). How chemical dependency can be perceived in the classroom (Background)

five-day model originally designed by Jim Crowley in Minnesota. Since the early 1980s Glenbeigh Hospital, a treatment center in northern Ohio, has adopted this model and trained hundreds of teachers in workshops to work with chemically dependent adolescents.

School personnel in the Project CARE school districts attend two training programs regularly:

1. Chemical Dependency Training and
2. Group Facilitator Training

Chemical Dependency Training provides skills in identifying chemically dependent behavior, avoiding professional enabling, motivating families to seek help and structuring a student assistance program in school. Group Facilitator Training gives guidance in running

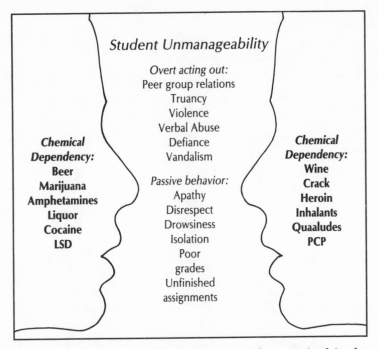

Figure 3(B). How chemical dependency can be perceived in the classroom (Figural)

insight and support groups for children involved with chemicals and children from alcohol/drug dependent or dysfunctional homes. Approximately 400 teachers in the Project CARE system receive training annually in these two training programs.

Both of these workshops are powerful experiences, which often change the lives of the participants. For example, many participants come to realize that they themselves are children or grandchildren of alcoholics, and this awareness offers them a new insight into their life experience.

Core Teams And Student
Assistance Program Coordinators

Core Teams are groups of trained teachers and counselors who assume responsibility for coordinating help for the abusing/addicted and co-dependent students. Presently there are over 300 of these groups in operation in more than 100 school districts in Project CARE. A Student Assistance Program (SAP) Coordinator or Chemical Dependency (CD) Coordinator, perhaps holding a degree in education, guidance and counseling or social work, assumes responsibility for the Student Assistance Program (SAP) services in the schools with the help of the Core Team.

Some schools have only Core Teams; others have only a Coordinator, and some have both. Each method has advantages and disadvantages. Use of a Core Team helps spread the responsibility so that more people take ownership in the program, and burnout of personnel is reduced. However, a Core team is a committee, and some committees have difficulty progressing from discussion to action. A SAP Coordinator can act more quickly and decisively, but other school personnel may take no ownership in the program and may let the SAP Coordinator do all the work. A combination of a Core Team and a SAP Coordinator utilizes the best of both and minimizes the disadvantages of each. Large school districts may have an SAP coordinator for the district and a Student Assistance Counselor plus a Core Team for each student building. Although staff members may volunteer in their initial enthusiasm following training, Core Teams and SAP Coordinators need to be compensated, as coaches are, with a decrease in academic responsibilities or an increase in pay.

Core Teams and SAP Coordinators have four primary functions:

1. To provide information to students and faculty
2. To identify students who need help

3. To motivate families to seek help
4. To provide support for recovering addicts and co-dependents

The Core Team and SAP Coordinator assume a leadership role in increasing the level of awareness in the community and school faculty. Core Teams regularly sponsor community education series on adolescent chemical use, children of alcoholics and the recovery process. Often community probation officers, youth workers and concerned parents participate on Core Teams and help carry the message back into the community. An educated community is less likely to enable young addicts to continue using without consequences. The Core Team also sponsors faculty in-service workshops to help faculty identify troublesome behavior, fill out behavioral observation forms and support children in recovery.

The leadership role of the Core Team and SAP Coordinator is vital in energizing the student assistance program. The Core Team and Coordinator are the force that connects the parents, students, faculty and community agencies in providing appropriate services to students who need assistance.

Behavioral Observation Forms And Referral Process

The referral process is the means by which school staff refer children to the Core Team and by which the Core Team refers children to an outside agency for evaluation. In order for this process to be used by staff it must be confidential, safe and efficient.

Students are identified through the use of behavioral observation forms, which list student behaviors that interfere with learning. These forms are filled out by teachers or other staff members who are concerned about children's unusual or inappropriate behavior and are collected by Core Teams or a SAP Coordinator. (See Appendix for Sample Behavioral Checklist.)

These forms indicate specific behavior on specific dates by a specific witness so they can be used to intervene and to confront the parent. Without this information the Core Team and SAP Coordinator cannot act.

These forms **DO NOT** diagnose or indicate alcohol/chemical dependency or any other specific dysfunction. They list only behavior, which may be motivated by a variety of causes. An outside professional, not the school, must diagnose the cause of the inappropriate behavior.

Although observing and recording student behavior is not a new concept, many teachers are hesitant to use a behavioral checklist for the following reasons:

1. Behavior is a matter of individual taste that should not be judged by teachers of another generation.
2. The recording of unusual student behavior is a subjective invasion of student privacy.
3. Records of behavior (all students may have unusual behavior at times) can be a source of possible unfair treatment of students.
4. Use of these forms can elicit parental anger and criticism.
5. Teachers, already burdened with excessive paper work, do not need to fill out more forms.
6. Observation of behavior, especially involving alcohol/chemical abuse, may be painful for teachers already involved with these problems, either as a dependent or a co-dependent.

In spite of these objections to behavioral observation forms, children with handicaps have a right to be identified and referred for help so that they can develop their full academic potential. The use of these forms seems to be one of the most efficient means for implementing this right.

With the information provided on behavioral observation forms the Core Team or SAP Coordinator can decide *what the next logical step is.* Contacting the parents for a meeting at school and registering concern usually comes first. (See Appendix for Sample Letter to Parents.) This may be difficult because children who are chemically dependent often have an alcoholic parent or grandparent. This inspection of children's chemical use may mean intervening on two or three generations worth of alcoholism, enabling and co-dependency. Parents may use denial or feigned compliance to resist change.

The process of motivating parents to seek help consists of first reviewing the data of the behavioral observation forms and sharing concern about the behavior. Next parents need to know that this behavior cannot continue in school. Third, an assessment by outside professionals is recommended to determine the cause of the inappropriate behavior. (See Appendix for Sample Consent for Release of Confidential Information and for Sample Assessment Contract.)

Schools cannot assume that children are chemically dependent, and yet chemical dependency is the first condition that should be ruled out by a professional. At this point some parents whose denial is not too strong will seek help. Others will need more motivation.

The parents who refuse to have their children evaluated by a professional often find denial of the problem safer because honesty might open up other family secrets, such as parental addiction, incest or battering, which are too frightening to acknowledge. These families can usually be motivated to seek help when their children have collected enough inappropriate behaviors that they are about to be suspended. When given a choice between assessment and suspension, most parents choose assessment.

When the school recommends a treatment center, agency or therapist for assessment based on the behavioral observation forms, it is important to choose an organization or individual that understands chemical dependency and is able to diagnose a wide range of other adolescent emotional problems. Core Teams and SAP

Coordinators must be familiar with the professionals in the area and know the quality of their work.

An evaluation should first rule out the possibility of chemical dependency in the children or in the children's parents because these are the two most common causes of academic and social dysfunction. If these two conditions do not exist, the counselor doing the evaluation should check any and all other possibilities of adolescent dysfunction. Children may be grieving an important loss, may have difficulty in adjusting to a new school, may be reacting to parental divorce or may have a serious personality disorder. Only an outside professional can diagnose students and suggest an appropriate course of treatment for the children and their families.

When children return to school after treatment, the Core Team or SAP Coordinator is available for continued support and monitoring as reintegration into the school culture is begun. This is a very difficult time for recovering adolescent addicts. Adult alcoholics can choose to not go back into the same bar with the same friends where they used to buy liquor. Children are not as lucky. Children must return to the school where they used to buy drugs and must learn to say no in the company of their old "using" friends. At this stage the Core Team or SAP Coordinator becomes a safe group/ person from which newly sober children can get support to maintain their sobriety.

7

Curricula And Programs (Support Groups)

Schools that wish to reduce student addiction have developed curricula and programs to help achieve a drug-free environment. These curricula and programs address the three goals of prevention, intervention and support. Prevention programs help prevent students from taking their first drink or drug during their school years. Intervention programs help prevent students from continuing their drinking or drug use. Support programs help prevent students from relapsing into active drug or alcohol use.

Prevention Curricula

Primary prevention programs need to begin with children in grades K through five. During the ages from birth to 12 years of age, children develop the beliefs and attitudes they will carry through high school. Beginning a prevention program after sixth grade is too late. By the time children are 13 years old, they have listened to hours of radio and TV glamorizing lifestyles that involve alcohol and other drugs. In addition, they have heard many older children, including older siblings, talk of the wonders of the drinking/drug experience. A prevention program that starts with a unit in tenth grade health class will not be effective.

Prevention programs for young children involve the use of special curricula designed for grades K through six. The contents of these curricula include exercises and lessons that teach children about:

1. Different types of families
2. Feelings and defenses
3. Problem-solving techniques
4. Self-esteem
5. Effects of alcohol and drugs on peoples' moods
6. Social skills and refusal skills

One of the best known curricula is "Children Are People," a series of lessons planned to help children develop self-concepts and choices that they can use to avoid mood-altering chemicals and other self-defeating behavior. Children who can talk about hurt and anger have many more choices than children who are filled with anger but cannot talk about it. Strong emotions that are not identified and shared are often medicated by a drug, such as alcohol, or a compulsive behavior, such as eating, work or sex.

Teen Institute

A prevention program for secondary school students that has been successful in Ohio is Teen Institute. This involves a weekend commitment by teenage students

and dedicated staff. Students listen to lectures, participate in exercises and share their feelings in group
experiences. All these activities are designed to help
students become more aware of their feelings and the
defenses they use to cover them. Feelings that are not
expressed directly may hide behind compulsive behavior.
Students develop a greater self-awareness, plus an
understanding of how chemical dependency affects
families. Using the enthusiasm and awareness generated
by spending a weekend together and sharing feelings,
the students then go back into their schools and develop
activities to share this information with other students.
The theory behind this approach is that often students
can learn from other students more easily than they can
learn from authority figures. This process has been
particularly effective when secondary school students
share with elementary school children. Listening to 15-
year-olds who have experienced Teen Institute may be
much more convincing for fourth graders than listening
to their adult teachers.

Prevention curricula, such as "Children Are People,"
and programs, such as Teen Institute, have helped
thousands of children avoid the first drink and drug
while in school, as well as develop healthy choices and a
positive self-image.

Intervention And Support Groups

Intervention and support involve the use of groups in
the middle/junior high school and high school levels. The
groups that are represented in most of northeast Ohio's
Project CARE schools are:

1. Awareness Groups
2. Insight Groups
3. Recovery Support Groups
4. Concerned Persons' Groups

Awareness Groups

Awareness Groups provide a forum for students who would like to discuss their concerns and get some direction for their lives. Such a group is open to students who have any problem. The group is not defined as an alcohol or drug awareness group, although many of the students who attend Awareness Groups are having drug-related problems or are children from alcoholic homes. As these students with drug abuse issues begin to emerge, they receive help in clearly defining these issues, and, when necessary, they can be referred to an outside professional for further evaluation. Similarly, children from painful or alcoholic families can be referred to an outside agency or to a group in school that can offer support.

Insight Groups

Insight Groups are being used in most Project CARE schools as a form of intervention and an alternative to suspension; they are designed for students who are in trouble because of some behavior relating to alcohol or drugs. In the past when students were caught for some drug-related offense, such as possession of drugs (or paraphernalia) or under the influence, they were automatically suspended from school. This suspension removed the user from the school, making possible further substance abuse, but not addressing the use itself.

Insight Groups reveal information to students about the signs and symptoms of chemical dependency and allow time for open discussion by students about chemical use. These groups are comprised of students who have chosen Insight over suspension and by students who may be curious about their own use and its meaning.

Students who enter an Insight Group must sign a *No-Use Contract*, which states they will remain drug free during the eight to ten weeks the group usually lasts.

Students who cannot remain drug free during their Insight experience need help and should be referred to a professional alcohol/chemical dependency counselor or agency. Allowing students to remain in an Insight Group after breaking their *No-Use Contract* is a form of professional enabling. This enabling may make the facilitator feel important and needed, but allows students' drinking/using to progress to a more serious condition.

As students listen to signs and symptoms of chemical dependency and begin sharing their own experiences, many reveal a harmful relationship with chemicals. If students admit that they have many of the symptoms of a disease, they need to be referred to the appropriate professionals instead of being given only punitive consequences. These professionals will be necessary to help provide the motivation to the students to attain and maintain sobriety. For an example of an Insight Group curriculum, see Appendix.

Recovery Support Groups

Recovery Support Groups in the Project CARE system are designed to help children who are trying to stay sober in a using/drinking world. These children have usually returned from an inpatient treatment facility, but may also be children struggling to stay sober with the help of outpatient counseling or Alcoholics Anonymous.

Recovery Support Groups are not group therapy. Their goal is to provide a supportive environment but not in-depth psychotherapy. Recovery Support Groups provide newly recovering students with a place where they can talk about the emotions of returning to school, finding a new peer group and readjusting to academic life in their sober state. Students who decide to remain clean and sober are a minority of the high school population. They are exhibiting statistically "deviant and abnormal behavior" by staying abstinent and they need a chance to share feelings about this new experience. Feelings that are not shared may be medicated again by a chemical or another compulsive behavior.

All children (and adults) who are chemically dependent and begin living a sober lifestyle will experience feelings of profound grief during their first year of abstinence. Children who let go of their addiction have to say goodbye to more emotional ties than most adults will ever have to. These children may say goodbye to the comfort of being high; to their using comrades who were their only friends; to their using boyfriend or girlfriend; to old habits, hangouts and music; to the old self-image; to old attitudes and to old dreams. Giving up any one of these things would be traumatic for most people. Giving up all of these is devastating; and yet, that is what recovering children must do, often with fewer emotional resources than nonaddicted children. Sobriety is not an easy task and can only be accomplished one day at a time.

Because this task is enormous and because the learning curve is steep in initial recovery, it is not surprising that most children relapse once before attaining a stable sobriety. Relapse or return to active drinking/using should not be seen as treatment failure or lack of character on the part of the recovering child. Relapse is the way many children gather more information as they come to believe that they really are chemically dependent and can't use without trouble. Sobriety involves practice, practice, practice.

Concerned Persons' Groups

The final type of group that most Project CARE schools provide is the Concerned Persons' Group. This group does not focus on students who are in trouble with alcohol or drugs. Concerned Persons' Groups are for children who come from homes with a parent or sibling who has a drinking/drug problem or from homes that are experiencing another type of pain, such as a divorce, death, loss or any kind of chronic physical or emotional illness. Understandably, students who are preoccupied with the emotional pain of their home life have less energy to devote to their school work. Energy used to repress emotional pain cannot be used to study algebra or gerunds. Therefore, the purpose of this group is to allow students to share feelings that may be blocking their concentration in school. As feelings are identified and shared, energy can be released to concentrate on school work.

Concerned Persons' Groups are usually limited to between 8 and 10 sessions and contain about eight members. Groups often begin with a short didactic piece about feelings, defenses or some aspect of chemical dependency and co-dependency, followed by time for the group to relate and share feelings. This process allows group members to share forbidden emotions like sadness, shame and anger, as well as to develop new ways to manage these feelings. This group also offers children new ways to live around the family dysfunction, ways that allow them to not feel responsible for the family pain and to develop a healthier self-esteem.

Children are referred to Concerned Persons' Groups by teachers, counselors, parents or themselves. These groups are exciting and liberating for children from painful families and may help prevent self-destructive behavior.

All of these, Awareness Groups, Insight Groups, Recovery Support Groups and Concerned Persons' Groups provide education and support, not therapy. Schools can best provide education and support; whereas, treatment centers and agencies can best provide therapy. The school groups are staffed by members of the Core Team or SAP Coordinator, people who have attended both a basic, five-day chemical dependency training program and a group facilitator training program. Facilitators are teachers and counselors, who enjoy relating to adolescents on an emotional level and who act as role models for healthy lifestyles.

Twelve-Step Groups

The use of Twelve-Step Groups by high school students has increased since the 1970s. Twelve-Step Groups include Alcoholics Anonymous, Narcotics Anonymous, Al-Anon, Alateen and Overeaters Anonymous. These fellowships exist in almost every community in the United States and are the most effective resource for long-term recovery from any kind of compulsive behavior. Many schools have donated space for outside AA or Alateen groups to meet during school time so that students can participate. Many more students attend AA and Alateen after school hours in their communities. Twelve-Step Groups are voluntary associations, which cooperate but are not affiliated with any organization or institution. Knowing the time, place and character of available Twelve-Step Groups in a community is essential for any Core Team or SAP Coordinator.

Many schools are nervous about referring students to Alcoholics Anonymous, the oldest and largest Twelve-Step Fellowship, because of old stereotyped images of "drunks." However, just as every other institution in American society, AA has been influenced by the invasion of the Baby Boom generation, the 40 million children born between 1946 and 1956. The unique characteristics of the Baby Boom are its size, level of education, sexual equality and chemical dependency. (See Figure 4.) In 1976 the Boom began to turn 30 years old, an age described as causing crisis and reevaluation of one's life choices. For some this crisis/reevaluation period means addressing an addiction begun in college or earlier. (See Table 4.)

As the Boom invaded AA, it brought with it its enormous size. Baby Boomers flooded in from the streets and from the treatment centers and their average age became younger and younger. AA groups grew and split like multiplying cells. The college-educated Boomers began using treatment and textbook jargon at meetings and women began taking an equal place in AA.

Figure 4. Annual births in the United States from 1910-1980

Table 4. Projection of population in the United States through 2010
Population in millions/age group

Year	5-17	18-24	25-34	35-44	45-54	55-64
1960	**44.2**	16.1	22.9	24.2	20.6	15.6
1970	52.5	**24.7**	25.3	23.1	23.3	18.7
1980	46.0	29.5	**36.2**	25.7	22.7	21.2
1990	45.3	25.2	41.1	**36.6**	25.3	20.8
2000	51.1	24.7	34.5	41.3	**35.6**	23.2
2010	48.5	28.4	36.3	34.7	40.6	**32.9**

* The projections used here are based on an average level of completed childbearing of
2.1 children per mother.

Bold numbers indicate Baby Boomers.

Finally the Boomers brought "drugs" into AA and the "dually addicted" AA member became common. Alcoholics Anonymous, like all other institutions in American society, experienced the turmoil of trying to swallow the enormous numbers of the Boom and their different life experiences and now is beginning to assimilate the children of the Boom.

For many adolescent addicts, AA is now the healthiest and most loving family they have. Adolescent addicts who are children of alcoholics find serenity, warmth, friendship and love in the AA program and the other Twelve-Step Fellowships. Educators must learn how to use these valuable resources by attending open meetings, learning about the Twelve Steps, and supporting Twelve-Step attendance.

Teaching Feelings And Using Groups

Many educators wonder why they should be so concerned with all this talk about feelings and personal growth groups and wonder what happened to learning about facts and teaching the regular academic curriculum with excellence. The answer is that as long as chemically dependent students remain in class, teachers will not be able to give full attention to teaching their curriculum.

Another concern is the need to develop the job skills that will be most necessary for children in our present economy. In previous generations, when we lived in an industrial economy, the most important job skill was the ability to work with things, ie., coal, steel or cars. Today we live in a postindustrial economy in which the majority of our labor force produces and distributes service and information. In a service and information economy the most important skill necessary to get and keep a job is the ability to work with other people in a healthy and productive way. Working with people's feelings is the primary job skill in this type of economy. This job skill is not being stressed in our high schools; our academic curriculum still reflects the priorities of an industrial economy, instead of a service and information economy.

A generation ago emotional education occurred primarily in the home. As divorce and single-parent families become increasingly common in the United States, many children will miss having their emotional needs attended to as parents are preoccupied with their own cycles of conflict. Therefore, many children will not have the emotional skills to handle an economy that will increasingly demand more emotional skills. When children don't get their needs met from people, they learn to get their needs met from things, chemicals and compulsive behavior, and they will teach their children to do the same.

Personal Growth Groups are probably the best settings in which to teach the intra- and interpersonal skills necessary to function in our present economy. These same skills are also badly needed to help couples manage the intensity of small nuclear families. Thus, the children of alcoholics and adolescent addicts have brought to the schools a form of affective education through their support groups. This form of education can be beneficial to the entire school body. In the future there is hope that all children will be able to use a group in school to identify their troublesome feelings, their most used defenses and their most useful talents and skills.

8

Support For
Co-dependent Teachers

Mankind has a history of making new technological devices, discovering they are dangerous and then trying to eliminate or control them. We have yet to successfully eliminate any new ideas of technology including the new ways children have found to alter consciousness. Bearing this in mind, it appears doubtful that we will completely eliminate adolescent chemical dependency, even with the best prevention programs. This means teachers will be working and living in the presence of this active disease for many years, probably forever. If by some miracle addictive drugs could be eliminated entirely, teachers would still have to work with behavior problems resulting from other kinds of dysfunctional families.

All teachers working in a chemically dependent classroom or a painful class will develop some characteristics of co-dependency. The characteristics of co-dependency will include denial, control, repressed anger, fear, self-doubt and shame. These will affect the teaching ability and self-image of any teacher. Managing the characteristics will differ depending on whether the teacher was raised in a relatively healthy family of origin, or a painful or alcoholic family of origin. (All alcoholic families are painful but not all painful families are alcoholic.)

Teachers With Functional Backgrounds

Teachers who were raised in a relatively healthy home will be aware at once if their classroom is dysfunctional because they know what a healthy system feels like. They will not enable the dysfunction by developing an increased tolerance for inappropriate behavior; they will maintain stable realistic boundaries for the children and will administer consistent consequences. Anger will be expressed appropriately and clearly as it arises. Such teachers will not accept blame from students or assume responsibility for the dysfunctional class.

Teachers who learned healthy coping skills at home will not need as much help as teachers who didn't learn these skills as a child. Teachers from a functional home will need education about the disease of chemical dependency, co-dependency and family systems. With this new awareness these teachers will be able to see how the whole class responds to chemical dependency, and they will become aware of ways they may have perpetuated the unhealthy class behavior. This awareness will usually be liberating and will result in new behavior for teachers and class members.

Teachers will need a place and time to vent feelings with each other about working in a chemically dependent and co-dependent school system and to share ideas about how to implement new chemical dependency policies and programs. This process of learning, sharing and planning will:

1. Need to be done regularly to stay current with the changing student population
2. Will help most co-dependent teachers from functional homes return to their classrooms with clear heads and motivation to teach.

Teachers With Dysfunctional Backgrounds

The process of learning, sharing and planning will not be as easy for teachers who were raised in a painful, dysfunctional or alcoholic home. Such teachers will walk into the classroom full of shame that they have carried for many years. Because they have spent years covering up family secrets and trying to control other people's behavior, their tolerance for inappropriate behavior may have increased to the point that they aren't sure what is normal. They may be afraid of their own anger and their students' anger, and may try to avoid each by enabling or caretaking. They may try to cover their own anxiety and shame by trying harder and harder to be good, thereby making them prime candidates for burnout. They may assume the blame for dysfunction in their classroom just as they did for the dysfunction in their own family of origin.

For these teachers, recovery means recovery from a lifetime of co-dependent behavior, not just a few years' worth. Teachers from dysfunctional families may be trying to get childhood intimacy needs met in their capacity as professional helper and friend. Their defense systems usually involve approval-seeking behaviors learned in childhood, which keep them and others unaware of their pain.

These teachers will need to:

1. Learn about chemical dependency and co-dependency

2. Find a place to share feelings
3. Set aside time to plan new classroom strategies just like teachers from more functional homes.

In addition they will need to begin dealing with a lifetime of co-dependent behavior and sort out the beliefs and feelings behind all their present behavior. This can best take place in a Twelve-Step Recovery Group such as Al-Anon and with a professional counselor.

Co-dependent teachers from painful families of origin will need to:

1. Identify the shame they carry from childhood and not hear the accusations of toxic students as further evidence of their inadequacy
2. Begin trusting their perceptions and feelings and find others who can validate them
3. Decide whether teaching, helping and managing others is a conscious vocational choice or an unconscious life script
4. Learn to recognize when they are being emotionally abused and learn to set limits to avoid further abuse
5. Learn how to express angry feelings appropriately when they occur and learn to hear student anger without experiencing the immobilization they felt as a child
6. Be aware of their workaholic tendencies and find healthy stress management and self-nurturing techniques
7. Detach themselves from the abuse of chemically dependent children and not accept blame for the inappropriate behavior
8. Learn to get intimacy needs met outside of work
9. Learn to identify approval-seeking defense strategies and make conscious choices about their use.

Co-dependent teachers will need to pay attention to their emotional health on a regular basis. As they begin to feel the old rigidity, fear and self-doubt return, they will need to share the feelings and practice new ways to nurture themselves. Co-dependency is an occupational hazard of any professional who works with chemical dependents, and it must be addressed and managed to maintain optimum work performance and peace of mind.

9

Hope For The Future

Chemical dependency and co-dependency are part of the fabric of every American high school. They are subtle yet powerful influences on the quality of education for our students. Chemical dependency and co-dependency are passed from generation to generation unless acknowledgment, intervention and prevention are exercised.

Our high schools of the future can capably manage the dilemma of chemical dependency and co-dependency in the classroom through the effective use of student assistance programs, such as Project CARE with its method of:

1. Developing school policy about chemical abuse
2. Training school staff

3. Forming Core Teams
4. Hiring Student Assistance Program Coordinators
5. Using behavioral observation forms
6. Utilizing the referral process to enlist the expertise of outside professionals
7. Developing pertinent curricula and programs

By managing this dilemma, schools of the future will be able to help children complete the difficult journey from dependent adolescents to independent adults. Further, the schools will be able to provide support for the chemically dependent and co-dependent children who come from families with a history of alcohol/drug abuse or other dysfunctions. It is also hopeful that the school staff will be able to maintain their own emotional health so that they, in turn, can help students deal with their feelings more effectively, thereby preparing them to work in our service- and information-oriented economy.

We can exert a positive influence on our society and school systems of the future by initiating the needed changes today.

APPENDIX A

Samples For Implementing
A Student Assistance Program

Sample School Board Policy
On Student Drug/Alcohol Abuse*

The Board of Education recognizes chemical dependency, including alcoholism, as a disease that is treatable. While the Board recognizes that health problems of youth are primarily the responsibility of the home, community and schools share in that responsibility because chemical dependency problems can interfere with behavior, learning and the fullest possible development of the student.

---

* Used with permission from Akron Public Schools.

The Board of Education is committed to achieving an environment free of chemical abuse or dependency within our student/faculty community. This goal cannot be achieved alone, regardless of funding, staff ability or program development. The family, churches, police, community health agencies, concerned citizens and the entire community must also play a role if our goal is to be accomplished.

The school staff is encouraged to play a major role in detection and referral of suspected chemical use, abuse and dependence. Specifically, school personnel are encouraged to become aware of the symptoms of chemical use, abuse and dependency and to be knowledgeable as to what steps to take when they reasonably believe that a student may be using or abusing alcohol or other chemicals. Staff members are encouraged to refer students experiencing chemical-related problems to the school counselor, the building principal or his designee. Through one of these sources, the staff will present to the student and his/her parent alternatives for chemical dependency assessment, diagnosis and possible treatment. In this regard, the staff shall be knowledgeable of resources provided by various community agencies, and this information shall be transmitted to parents and students.

In fulfilling the staff role involving awareness, detection and referral, the administrative staff is encouraged to develop informational materials and in-service programs for teachers and others coming into direct contact on a daily basis with our student population.

In cases where a student is found to be using or possessing drugs or alcohol on school grounds or at school-sponsored events, the school personnel have the responsibility to enforce the school's "Code of Student Behavior." This means that these students may be subject to suspension or expulsion from the school. However, building administrators are encouraged to develop a procedure that will cause each case to be reviewed on its individual merits, and if the parents and the student are willing to become involved in an educational program concerning chemical use/abuse and/or to seek professional help, the degree or type of punishment may be tempered by such an agreement to seek help.

Sample School Board Policy On Chemical Dependency For School Employees*

The School District recognizes chemical dependency as a treatable illness. For purposes of this policy, chemical dependency is defined as an illness in which an employee's consumption of mood-altering chemicals repeatedly interferes with job performance and adversely affects health.

If the employee refuses to accept diagnosis and treatment, or fails to respond to treatment, and the result of such refusal or failure is such that job performance continues to be affected, it will be handled in the same manner that similar refusal or treatment failure would be handled for any other illness. Implementation of this policy will not require or result in any special regulations, privileges or exemptions from the standard administrative practice applicable to job performance requirements.

Supervisors and administrators will implement this policy in such a manner that an employee with chemical dependency will not have job security or promotional opportunity affected either by diagnosis itself or by the employee's request for treatment.

The confidential nature of the medical records of employees with chemical dependency shall be preserved in the same manner as for all other medical records.

---

* *Used with permission from Akron Public Schools.*

Sample Administrative Regulation:
Procedure For Handling Instances Of Possession, Sale, Distribution Or Use Of Drugs Or Alcohol By Students*

Introduction

The presence and use of alcohol, drugs, counterfeit drugs and other intoxicating substances (hereinafter "controlled substances") pose a continuing threat to the school community and to the intellectual, social, mental, physical and emotional health and development of students in the School System. The purpose of these regulations is to implement the policy of the Board of Education, which prohibits students from using, possessing, offering for sale or distributing controlled substances in the following situations:

1. While in school buildings
2. While on school grounds
3. While at school-sponsored events
4. While being transported to or from school or school-sponsored events
5. In any other situation where such students are subject to the authority of the School

All employees within the School System are expected to take an active role in reducing or eliminating the threat posed by the presence and use of controlled substances through the implementation of preventative measures and through intervention when the possession, use, sale or distribution of controlled substances has become apparent. The two aspects of this regulation, prevention and intervention, are explained in greater detail below.

Prevention

All employees of the School System are expected to aid in the prevention of student possession and use of controlled substances. Prevention is best accomplished by seeking to foster student self-esteem and morale, by educating students and community members of the symptoms and effects of use of controlled substances and by publicizing the legal and educational consequences of possession or use thereof.

Each employee of the School System should familiarize himself/herself with, and seek to utilize, the following resources available to assist in the prevention of use of controlled substances:

1. Student support services available in the School System such as counselors, psychologists, the Pupil Adjustment Program and the Student/ Staff/Parent Outreach Services Program
2. Programs designed to support behavioral change for students who have used, or may be inclined to use, controlled substances due to their perceived or actual inability to cope with their life circumstances
3. Peer groups/programs designed to provide students with the knowledge and training needed to deal with the controlled substance problem that exists in the school and community settings
4. School experiences designed to provide students with a feeling of success, accomplishment and high self-esteem
5. Educational programs for students, staff, parents and the community in general whereby an awareness can be developed of the signs, symptoms and effects of the use of controlled substances, including, but not limited to, orientation programs for students, teachers and parents, together with other activities and materials that reinforce or supplement these orientation programs.

Intervention

The Board of Education prohibits the use, possession, sale or distribution of controlled substances by students except for supervised, prescribed medications taken pursuant to the instructions of a licensed physician. The Code of Student Behavior, which is annually provided to each student in the School System, expresses this prohibition and advises the student of the consequences.

The first step in the intervention process is the identification of students who may be affected by their own use, possession, sale or distribution of controlled substances, or by that of others in the school or community. All employees of the School System shall report any circumstances which they believe to be indicative of the use, sale, possession or distribution of controlled substances to the principal of the school in which the student is enrolled. Sources of information relating to these suspicious circumstances include:

1. Communications with the student's family
2. Observations/documentation by administrators, teachers, counselors or other school staff members (see Behavioral Checklist)
3. Admissions by the student or by his peers
4. The results of evaluations performed by community agencies specializing in the treatment of problems related to controlled substances.

The following procedure shall be utilized when employees of the School System become aware of the circumstances that are indicative of the use, sale, possession or distribution of controlled substances, but where controlled substances are not discovered:

1. When an employee of the School System becomes aware of circumstances indicative of the use, possession, sale or distribution of controlled substances, he or she shall report the circumstances to the principal of the school.
2. When the principal has information sufficient to warrant a reasonable belief that the student may be involved with the use, possession, sale or distribution of controlled substances, he or she

shall have a conference with the student and the student's parent or legal guardian (unless the parent or legal guardian refuses to attend). The purpose of this conference is to identify any problems the student may have, whether related to controlled substances or not, and to establish a plan leading to more constructive behavior.

3. If, in the opinion of the principal, the student is involved in the use, possession, sale or distribution of controlled substances, the student's parent or legal guardian will be advised and encouraged to seek professional advice. The student and his/her parent or legal guardian shall be referred to seek an evaluation from a community agency specializing in treatment of problems arising from the use of controlled substances. (See your local list of agencies.)

A different situation altogether is presented when school authorities become aware of the actual use, possession, sale or distribution of controlled substances while a student is subject to the authority of the school. As described below, there is a distinction between cases whereby the *sale or distribution* of controlled substances is made or attempted, and those instances where *simple possession or use* are involved.

1. Where a student is found to have been *selling or distributing* controlled substances:
   a. The principal will contact the parent or legal guardian of the student.
   b. The principal *must* notify the local police department (per Code of Student Behavior) and/or other appropriate authorities and submit all evidence and other pertinent information.
   c. The principal will recommend to the superintendent that the student be expelled.
2. Where a student is found to have *used, possessed or received* controlled substances:

a. The principal will contact the parent or legal guardian of the student.

b. The principal has the discretion to provide a warning on the first infraction, depending on his/her evaluation of the totality of the circumstances surrounding the incident, together with any other information which may come to his/her attention.

c. The principal *may* notify the local police department or other appropriate authorities (the principal should feel free to contact the superintendent both for his/her judgment and so that he/she may obtain legal advice if he/she thinks it appropriate to do so).

d. The student *may* be suspended for up to 10 days in accordance with the procedures identified in the Code of Student Behavior.

e. Students who are willing to become involved in insight groups (anti-drug/alcohol educational sessions) or undergo a professional controlled substance dependency evaluation and, if necessary, begin rehabilitation may be released from the maximum suspension.

f. Controlled substance dependency evaluations and rehabilitation programs shall be conducted by agencies or persons who are recognized authorities in this field, at the expense of the student's parent or legal guardian.

g. When a student is willing to have a professional dependency evaluation:

    1) The parent or legal guardian of the student shall notify the school principal that the student has made contact and is willing to comply with the evaluation and treatment process. The Assessment Contract must be completed and returned to the school by the student's parent or guardian. (See copy of the Consent for the Release of Confidential Information and Assessment Contract.)

2) Based on evidence of prompt application and acceptance to a community agency for evaluation and treatment, or attendance in an insight group, the principal may excuse the student from the maximum suspension. Students who refuse evaluation or who terminate such treatment or attendance at an insight group before successful completion may be suspended for the remainder of the original suspension.

3) Students should attend school if they are receiving primary treatment on an outpatient basis and can function appropriately in a school setting.

3. For repeated offenses of use, possession or receipt of controlled substances, the principal will normally:
   a. Recommend to the superintendent that the student be expelled
   b. Notify the parents or legal guardian, the local police department and/or other appropriate authorities regarding the student's use and/or possession of controlled substances

4. Repeated offenses shall be reviewed in the context of the student's age, maturity and history of appropriate behavior since the first offense.

Sample Behavioral Checklist*

Student's Name _____ Date _____

Concerned Person's Signature _____

Relationship to Student _____

Concern for the above student has been expressed by his or her family, friend(s), another staff member or administrator. In an effort to ascertain what the student's behavior indicates, your observations would be extremely valuable. Please rate behavior and/or changes in behavior in the following areas. Add as many details as you can about your *observation*. All information is confidential. You are not being asked to accuse, label or diagnose. You are being asked to note your concern.

This document does not become a part of the student's permanent record. It will be used to help the student and his/her family to clarify the concern and to help the family decide on appropriate action. You will receive a response note from the Core Team within two to ten days.

Your observations are appreciated.

CURRENT STATUS

Please circle current grade: A   B   C   D   F   Any change?   Yes _____ No _____

If yes, please explain: _____

_____

_____

Have you seen any of these signs or behaviors?

BEHAVIOR	**ACADEMIC**
_____ Generally cooperative	_____ Often frustrated
_____ Inconsistent behavior	_____ Cheating
_____ Withdrawn, seclusion	_____ Extreme dissatisfaction
_____ Class clown	with school
_____ Sleeps in class	_____ High achiever
_____ Obscene language, gestures	_____ Is doing satisfactory or
_____ Argumentative	better
_____ Lying	_____ Sudden decline in grades
_____ Boasts "partying,"	_____ No effort
"getting high"	_____ Irresponsible
_____ Possesses paraphernalia	_____ Short attention span
_____ Writes/draws chemical graffiti	_____ Academic failure
_____ Mood swings	_____ Lacks motivation
_____ Reads chemical literature	

ATTENDANCE

_____ Regularly attends class
and is not tardy
_____ Frequent absences
_____ Frequent tardies
_____ Frequent requests to go
to restroom
_____ Found in inappropriate
places on school
grounds/in building
_____ Ran away from home

APPEARANCE/HEALTH

_____ Appears healthy
_____ Neglects personal
appearance
_____ Glassy, bloodshot eyes
_____ Lacks coordination
_____ Slurred speech
_____ Cough (constant,
persistent)
_____ Frequently complains
of illness
_____ Smells of alcohol
_____ Smells of pot
_____ Lethargic
_____ Memory loss
_____ Chemical/smoke odors
_____ Low stamina

RELATIONSHIPS

_____ Student's close friends are:

_____

_____

_____

_____

SOCIAL BEHAVIOR

_____ Appears well adjusted/happy
_____ Change in friends — negative
_____ Sudden popularity
_____ Avoids peers
_____ Seldom expresses feelings/
emotions
_____ Peer exclusion
_____ Defensive with adults
_____ Bully with other students
_____ Family problems talked about
_____ Mentions abuse in family
_____ Speaks angrily of parents
_____ Paranoid (student feels
persecuted, picked on)
_____ Suffered recent loss in family
(death, divorce, moved)
_____ Frequently talks about
drugs/alcohol
_____ Usually has large amounts
of money
_____ Mentions sibling problems
_____ Depression
_____ Others talk about his or her
use of drugs/alcohol
_____ On probation with courts

EXTRA-CURRICULAR

_____ Regular participation (not
in any way disruptive)
_____ Cuts practice
_____ Loss of eligibility
_____ In danger of loss of eligibility
_____ Quit team/squad
_____ Quality of participation
declining

ADDITIONAL COMMENTS:

_____

_____

_____

_____

_____

Please return this form, in a sealed envelope,

TO: _____   BY: _____

---

* *Used with permission from Akron Public Schools.*

Sample Letter To Parents*

Dear Mr. & Mrs. _____:

We have advised you that your (son/daughter) has been charged with an infraction of the rules and regulations of the Board of Education by reason of claimed misconduct occurring on school premises on _____ (date). There is reason to believe that drugs or alcohol may have been involved in the incident for which the charge is made.

We have explained to you that the charge made, if true, could result in suspension or expulsion of your child from school for a period of time not exceeding the balance of this semester. We have explained also that the school desires to extend as much help as possible to children who may be involved in the use of drugs or alcohol and for that reason have adopted a program to provide support to those children who are chemically dependent. The program involves the use of a Core Team composed of school personnel and volunteers who provide on-site support and assistance for the child in overcoming or avoiding alcohol or drug use. This service is provided only as an assistance for treatment by qualified professionals and is not an alternative by which to substitute for such treatment.

You have elected to apply for evaluation and treatment of your child at _____ (agency name). By reason of this decision, the school will suspend any further proceedings relating to the claimed disciplinary infraction during the course of treatment at the agency. Upon discharge by reason of satisfactory completion of the course of treatment or the termination of the current school semester, whichever comes earlier, the charges will be dropped and no further action taken. You and your (son/daughter) should sign a copy of this letter if you consent and agree to the terms on which disciplinary proceedings are being suspended. Your signature to a copy of this letter does not constitute an admission of the charged misconduct nor an admission that your child abuses drugs or alcohol, nor will a refusal to sign be held against your (son/daughter) in any manner. The program being offered is purely voluntary and is available to those who seek to avoid drug or alcohol abuse as well as those who have already become users.

Very truly yours,

Principal

Consented and agreed:

_____   _____
                (Parent)   (Student)

Original to be filed in school office, yellow copy to counselor, pink copy to parent, goldenrod copy to Core Team.

---

* Used with permission from Akron Public Schools.

Sample Consent For The Release
Of Confidential Information*

I, _____ , freely authorize the Core Team of
　　　　　(name of student)

_____ to disclose to _____
　　(name of school)　　　　　　　　　　　　　　(Agency/Counselor)

upon request, any information which relates to the recommendations made by

this group for the purpose of a/an _____
　　　　　　　　　　　　　　　　　(chemical dependency evaluation)

I understand that I may revoke this consent at any time by written statement.

Executed this _____ day of _____, 19 _____.

_____
Signature of Student

_____
Signature of Parent, Guardian or
Authorized Representative

Original in school file, copy forwarded to Outreach Services, pink copy to student, goldenrod copy to counselor.

---

* *Used with permission from Akron Public Schools.*

Sample Assessment Contract*

1. I will make an appointment with an approved Assessment Agency/Counselor for an evaluation of my chemical use within five (5) school days.

2. I will attend the number of assessment sessions as scheduled during my first appointment at the Assessment Center.

3. I will comply with the program prescribed by the Assessment Center.

4. I give permission for the Assessment Agency/Counselor to provide notification of the following information to _____.
   (name of school)

   • Compliance with items 1, 2 and 3 above

   • Immediate notification of noncompliance with items 2 and 3 above

   • After completion of the formal assessment by a trained Chemical Dependency Agency/Counselor, the Agency must forward to _____ documentation of the following: (name of school)

   •• Completion of assessment
   •• Notification as to whether treatment is required

5. I agree to attend any in-school group sessions as required by the Core Team. A Core Team may be comprised of board-paid employees and volunteers, all of whom work pursuant to direction of the school.

6. I agree to abstain from the use of chemicals while attending assessment and during any prescribed program. I will not attend school, any school activity or any school function under the influence of any chemical.

Executed this _____ day of _____, 19 _____.

_____
Signature of Student

Approved:

Parent _____

Witness _____

Original in school file, yellow copy forwarded to the Assessment Agency/Counselor, pink copy to student, goldenrod copy to counselor

---

* Used with permission from Akron Public Schools.

Insight Group Curriculum

Pre-Insight Group Interview

Goal: Students will understand goals and rules of Insight Group as explained by an administrator and will receive contracts to be signed by parent and child.

Rationale: Students are referred to Insight Group either as a result of concerns generated by the behavioral checklist or as an alternative to in-school or out-of-school suspension. Students who attend Insight Group need to be externally motivated enough to comply with group rules. Having an administrator conduct a screening and orientation interview will reinforce the school's commitment to the Insight process and keep students' anger focused on the disciplinary process, not Insight.

Method: A letter is sent to a student's parents stating that the school offers a group guidance program designed to help students gain insight and make healthy choices in their lives. Parents are expected to sign agreements regarding their child's participation in Insight Group. Prospective group members will be interviewed by an administrator in charge of discipline before admission into the group.

Behavioral objectives:
1. Students and parents will sign an agreement to follow group rules (time, attendance, participation) or be discharged from the group.
2. Students and parents will sign an agreement that the student will attend Insight Group in place of in-school or

out-of-school suspension. Students
who do not comply with group rules or
facilitator recommendations will have
to serve their original suspension.

3. Students and parents will sign an
agreement that the student will use no
mood-altering chemicals for the dura-
tion of the Insight Group.

4. Students and parents will sign an
agreement to follow through with the
facilitators' recommendations within
30 days of being notified at the end of
Insight Group.

Session I: Introduction And Sibling Roles

Goal: Students will introduce themselves to the
group and state what behavior prompted
them to join Insight. Students will be able
to identify the four sibling roles, identify
their role with examples and identify how
the behavior that motivated them to Insight fits their role (Wegscheider-Cruse,
1981).

Rationale: Students enter Insight Group well-de-
fended and angry. They have been caught
getting into trouble again. Helping students identify with roles (especially
Scapegoat and Mascot) gives them insight
into their acting-out behavior and relationship with peers, cliques, siblings and
family. This takes the focus off of blam-
ing the bad boy or girl and gives meaning
to troublesome behavior. This exercise
also reminds students that they are children, not adults.

Method:	Teacher/facilitator will give short lecture on the four sibling roles (Hero, Scapegoat, Lost Child and Mascot) and then conduct discussion as students identify with roles.
Behavioral objectives:	1. Students will introduce themselves and state what behavior led them to Insight Group. 2. Students will be asked to identify themselves and their siblings with a role. 3. Students identifying with a particular role will gather in sub-groups and write how this role is helpful and hurtful to themselves and their families. 4. Students will state how the offense or crisis that motivated them to join the Insight Group represents a particular role behavior.

Session II: Family Map And Feelings

Goal:	Students will visualize their family relationships by drawing circles on a page to represent their family and best friend. Students will list three adjectives that describe each parent and step-parent plus three feelings they are most aware of having at home.
Rationale:	Students' anger and defensiveness concerning their "offense" can be further avoided by focusing on relationships within the family. Most students in Insight come from homes under stress. It is important for student, group and facilitator to identify stressors within the system (divorce, parental alcoholism, sibling rivalry). This exercise will begin students identifying feelings and using

feeling words. Feelings are often carried from home and brought to school. This exercise continues to reinforce the student as a child in a parental system and helps the group build trust as they share feelings of being children at home.

Methods: Teacher/facilitator will give instructions for exercise, coach students who need help and facilitate each student presenting his or her family and feelings to the group. Common feelings can be identified and discussed by the group. Stress of parental or sibling alcoholism can be noted.

Behavioral objectives:
1. Students will draw a picture of their family
   a. Size of circles will represent the power or influence of that person.
   b. Distance between circles will represent emotional closeness.
   c. Best friend is included to see importance of peer group influence.
2. Students will list three adjectives describing their parents and step-parents.
3. Students will list three feelings they most often feel at home.
4. Students will share their family picture and feelings with the group.

Session III: Feelings And Defenses

Goal: Students will identify three feelings they most often experience and ways they manage to cover up their feelings at home and at school.

Rationale: Most adolescents have never been taught how to identify feelings or defenses. Lacking the ability to verbalize feelings and identify defenses, some adolescents get into trouble for acting out unidentified feelings and using their defensive styles. The purpose of this session is to help students become aware of the defense systems they use to manage common uncomfortable feelings.

Method: Teacher/facilitator will hand out a list of common feeling words and defenses used to avoid feelings. Teacher/facilitator will review several feelings and defenses. Students will share examples in their own life of three feelings and defenses.

Behavioral objectives:
1. Students will identify three feelings that they experience most often (ie., hurt, fear, sadness, loneliness, shame or joy).
2. Students will identify three ways they defend themselves from their feelings (ie., denial, rationalizing, minimizing, blame or withdrawal).
3. Students will identify a recent time they used their defenses.
4. Students will identify the consequences of their defensive style.

Optional (depending on time)
1. Have students point out their peers' defenses.
2. Have students draw a picture of their favorite defense.
3. Have students role play an inside and outside self.
4. Have students role play a scene when they used a defense recently, e.g., the scene that got them into Insight.

Session IV: SMAST And Symptoms Checklist

Goal: Students will provide teacher/facilitator
                   with data about their drinking/drug use
                   and will start to share the extent of their
                   use and its consequences on home life and
                   school life.

Rationale: This exercise will provide the teacher/
                   facilitator with important information
                   about the student's use. The Short
                   Michigan Alcoholism Screening Test
                   (SMAST) provides an easy-to-score,
                   widely used instrument for detecting
                   harmful chemical use. A checklist of
                   symptoms provides similar data. Having
                   this information in writing will be useful
                   for later recommendations. Remember,
                   the words alcoholic or drug addict have
                   not been used. There should be no
                   attempt to label the child. This session
                   provides information for the group
                   leader and permission to start telling
                   "war stories" without fear of being
                   labeled.

Method: Teacher/facilitator will hand out
                   SMAST and checklist of symptoms to
                   students and explain questionnaire.
                   Teacher/facilitator will administer both
                   questionnaires by reading/explaining
                   each question/symptom. At completion
                   of questionnaire, leader will ask group to
                   share common using behaviors. Atten-
                   tion should be drawn to consequences
                   without using the words alcoholic or
                   addict. Students hand in questionnaires
                   to leader who scores SMAST test and
                   reviews symptoms checklist.

Behavioral objectives:
1. Students will check appropriate responses to SMAST and checklist of symptoms.
2. Students will state two characteristics of their using styles.
3. Students will identify one negative consequence of their use in their home life and school life.

Session V: Drinking/Drug History

Goal: Students will complete a drinking/drug history and identify progression and negative consequences from their use.

Rationale: Students need to see their drinking/drug history written down in black and white. *Seeing* a progression and negative consequences on paper makes them more real and allows the student to begin to make cause and effect inferences between his/her use and negative consequences. Increasing emphasis is placed on progression and negative consequences.

Method: Teacher/facilitator will explain the process of filling out a drinking/drug history. As students begin filling in their history, teacher/facilitator can make individual contact with students helping them to focus on progression and consequences. Time may allow for one student to read his/her history and receive feedback from group. Group leader can focus students' attention to particular symptoms and consequences and can illicit information by probing and confronting. Drinking/drug histories should be turned in to group leader who will

review them and compare to SMAST
and checklist of symptoms.

Behavioral   1. Students will complete a drinking/
objective: drug history.
     a. Students will write type of drug
       used, quantity and frequency.
     b. Students will write negative conse-
       quences with family, school, girl-
       friend, boyfriend and peers.
   2. Students will clarify drinking/drug
     history through probing from facilita-
     tor/leader.

Session VI: Feelings Chart

Goal: Students will be able to identify their
feelings on a feelings graph and verbal-
ize an understanding of how chemicals
can change one's mood. (Johnson, 1973)

Rationale: A feelings chart is introduced after
information has been collected regard-
ing students' use. This reduces student
anxiety and defensiveness about being
labeled alcoholic and allows teacher/
facilitator to use examples of students'
using in the lecture. The feelings chart
lecture should be tied back into three
feelings identified in Session II as well
as "morning after" feelings to illustrate
connection between stored-up, unexpressed feelings and using chemicals.

Method: Teacher/facilitator will give short
lecture on the feelings chart illustrat-
ing four phases of use: 1) learning, 2)
seeking, 3) harmful dependency and
4) using to feel normal. Teacher/
facilitator will also explain memory

impairment (blackout, euphoric recall) and delusion caused by denial, minimizing, blame, rationalization and projection. Teacher will ask each student to identify him/herself on the feelings chart at significant times of his/her life and to identify the defense he/she likes best.

Behavioral objective:

1. Students will use feelings chart to graph feelings in at least two significant times in their life.
2. Students will graph how chemicals have changed their mood on a specific occasion.
3. Students will be able to verbalize how dosage has affected swings in their mood.
4. Students will identify at least two defenses they find work best with parents and teachers.

Session VII: Disease Of Chemical Dependency

Goal:

Students will be able to explain how the potency of the drug combined with the genetic susceptibility of the user interact to create a progressive, chronic illness. Students will also identify memorable problem drinkers in their family.

Rationale:

Students need to be aware of the growing body of research that points to a genetic susceptibility to chemical dependency in some people (Milam, 1981). This idea will help reduce the belief that tolerance and control are a matter of willpower for all drinkers and will help reduce the shame associated with "irresponsible" alcoholic

drinking. The idea will also be a shame
reducer to children who have an alcoholic
parent or grandparent.

Method: Teacher/facilitator will present information on the biogenetic aspects of alcohol-
ism/addiction at a level students can
understand. Information can be presented through lecture or film. News-
paper articles on this subject, symptoms
of chemical dependency, can be presented
and discussed. Teacher/facilitator can ask
students to identify drug allergies or food
allergies they may have. Leader can also
ask students to identify drinking/drug
patterns in their families by using a 0
through 4 scale — 0 being a nonuser and
4 being alcoholic/addict.

Behavioral
objective:
1. Students will be able to explain the
   differing powers of various drugs.
2. Students will be able to explain and
   illustrate how heart disease, cancer,
   alcoholism and diabetes run in families.
3. Students will identify drinking/drug-
   using pattern of parents, grandparents
   and siblings on a 0 through 4 scale (0
   being a nonuser and 4 being alcoholic/
   addict).
4. Students will identify their using pattern on a symptoms check list.

Session VIII: Drinking/Drug History

Goal: Students will share their drinking/drug
history with the group. Group will provide feedback about defenses they see.
Facilitator/teacher will clarify progression, symptoms and consequences.

Rationale: Students continue seeing cause and effect relationship between their "problems" and their drug use. Patterns and progression of use can also be highlighted. Students begin to see "problems" as a part of a larger pattern and not just isolated incidents caused by other people. Students also begin to see relationship between their use and attaining their goals. Students give one another feedback on other's honesty and defenses. Teacher may use this exercise to gather information to decide about appropriate recommendations for students.

Methods: Teacher/facilitator facilitates each student's sharing of drinking/drug history and consequences. Teacher may probe for details and clarification and highlight progression, symptoms, negative consequences and how they impact student's life goals.

Behavioral objectives:
1. Students will have finished written drinking/drug history.
2. Students will share a history of their use and associated negative consequences with school, family, boyfriend/ girlfriend and peers.
3. Students will verbalize how using affects their goals.
4. Students will identify defenses one another use (i.e., denial, minimizing, blame or rationalizing).

Session IX: Evaluation

Goal: Students will state how they see chemicals affecting their life, whether they have a drug/alcohol problem, and what they will do to avoid social or academic problems in the future. Students and teacher/facilitator will give feedback to students regarding honesty and drug use.

Rationale: This exercise encourages students to integrate all they have learned and shared about their family, feelings and use of chemicals. Students can give feedback to each other about whether they think peers can control their use on their own. Teacher/facilitator can listen for how delusional or honest a student is about his/her drinking.

Method: Teacher/facilitator asks students to review for the group how they see their relationship with chemicals and how they will avoid social or academic problems in the future. Leader facilitates student feedback and challenges group denial or minimizing. Teacher/facilitator shares feedback and concern for group members who appear in trouble with their drug use. Specific feedback regarding recommendations for an assessment or follow-up counseling is given in an individual session after group.

Behavioral objective:
1. Students will identify their perception of their relationship with chemicals and their social or academic difficulties.
2. Students will state plans to avoid further problems.
3. Students will hear feedback from peers regarding their chemical use.
4. Students will hear feedback from teacher/facilitator about their relationship with chemicals.

Post-Group Interview

Goal: Students and parents who need additional help will be notified by the facilitator. Students and parents will listen to concerns of facilitator and follow through with recommendations for a professional assessment within 30 days.

Rationale: Insight Groups do not contain an average cross section of the student body. They contain a much higher than average percentage of chemically dependent children and children of alcoholics. Therefore, students in Insight Groups often need an additional assessment. The Insight Group curriculum uncovers valuable information that can be used in the assessment process.

Method: Insight Group teacher/facilitator identifies students who appear to need continued assessment. The parents of these students are asked to come to the school for a conference. Teacher/facilitator reviews concerns about student and makes formal recommendation for further assessment. Parents are reminded of the contract they signed at the beginning of group regarding recommendations of group leader.

**Behavioral
objective:**   1. Parents will attend Recommendation Conference.
                     2. Parents will listen to concerns and recommendations of group leader.
                     3. If parents cannot attend conference, they will listen to recommendations over the phone.
                     4. Parents will follow through with recommendations within 30 days of conference.

APPENDIX B

Symptoms Of Alcoholism/Chemical Dependency

I. Early Phase

1. Preoccupation
   — thinking about "partying" a lot
2. Blackout
   — not remembering pieces of the night before; chemically induced amnesia
3. Sneaking
   — sneaking or hiding chemicals; lying about when you use
4. Rapid Intake
   — gettin the drug into your system rapidly, i.e. gulping drinks
5. Defensiveness
   — refusal to talk about how much you drink/use

6. Guilt
   — feeling bad about drinking/using behavior
7. Increased Tolerance
   — the ability to use more than others without showing the effects.

II. Middle Phase

1. Loss of Control
   — drinking/using more than you intended
2. Alibis
   — always a good reason to have a drink/get high
3. Grandiosity
   — playing the big shot
   — always right
4. Periods of Abstinence
   — going on the wagon
5. Others Disapprove
   — family, friends, or lovers complain about user's moods and behavior
6. Mood Swings
   — Dr. Jeckyll and Mr. Hyde; nice when sober and mean when drinking, or vice versa
7. Change in Pattern
   — changing drugs to find one that doesn't create problems
8. Drug Centered Behavior
   a. friends — users socialize with users
   b. hobbies — hobbies provide a time to get high/drink
9. Self Pity
   — users often feel picked on and sorry for themselves
10. School/Job Problems
    — work becomes more difficult with a toxic brain
11. Resentments
    — toxic, irritated neurons perceive the world as a source of constant irritation
12. Geographic "Cure"
    — a belief that life would be OK if you worked or lived somewhere else
13. Family Adapts
    — family members compensate for the user's disability, i.e. take over chores the user used to do.
14. Changes in Eating
    — eating more or less depending on your drug of choice
15. Sex Problems
    — being sexual when you don't want to be or not being able

to be sexual when you do want to be
16. Jealousy
    — may become suspicious and possessive of mate's attention
    to other people

III. Late Phase

1. Protecting Supply
   — always know where to find a drink or drug
2. Hospitalization
   — for accidents, overdoses, suicide attempts
3. Morning Use
   — using after waking from sleep
4. Continuous Use
   — using when you don't have to be doing something else
5. Tremors
   — physically shaky hands or internal jitters
6. Legal Problems
   — DWI, fights, divorce, bad checks
7. Impaired Thinking
   — difficulty thinking as toxicity increases
8. Physical Problems
   — ulcers, hypertension, colds, heart problems, cirrhosis, hepatitis, lung cancer
9. Loss of Tolerance
   — getting high/drunk on much less than you used to need
10. Deterioration of Friends
    — friends reflect late stage using patterns
11. Fears
    — feeling afraid, nervous or anxious most of the time

Suggested Reading List

For Teachers, Counselors And Students

Alcoholism/Chemical Dependency

Alcoholics Anonymous. **Alcoholics Anonymous.** New York: Alcoholics Anonymous World Services, 1939, 1976.

Goodwin, Donald. **Is Alcoholism Hereditary?** 2nd ed., New York: Ballantine Books, 1976, 1988.

Gorski, Terence, and Miller, Merlene. **Staying Sober.** Independence, MO: Independence Press, 1986.

Jellinek, E. M. **The Disease Concept of Alcoholism.** New Haven: Hillhouse Press, 1960.

Johnson, Vernon. **I'll Quit Tomorrow.** New York: Harper & Row, 1973.

Kurtz, Ernest. **Not-God.** Center City, MN: Hazelden, 1979.

103

Milam, James, and Ketcham, Katherine. **Under the Influence.** New York: Bantam Books, 1981, 1983.

Milam, James. **The Emergent Comprehensive Concept of Alcoholism.** Kirkland, WA: ACA Press, 1974 (out of print).

Selzer, M. L.; Vinokor, A., and van Raaijen, L. 1975. "A Self-Assessment Short Michigan Alcoholism — Screening Test (SMAST)." *J. Stud. Alcohol, 36,* no. 1:117.

U.S. Department of Health and Human Services. **Alcoholism: An Inherited Disease.** Washington, DC: U.S. Government Printing Office, 1985.

Vaillant, George. **The Natural History of Alcoholism.** Cambridge, MA: Harvard University Press, 1983.

Children of Alcoholics And Co-dependence

Ackerman, Robert. **Children of Alcoholics: A Guidebook for Educators, Therapists, and Parents.** 2nd ed., Holmes Beach, FL: Learning Publications, 1978, 1983.

Alateen. **Hope for Children of Alcoholics.** New York: Al-Anon Family Groups, 1980.

Black, Claudia. **It Will Never Happen To Me.** Denver, CO: M.A.C. Printing, Publishing Division, 1982.

Carnes, Patrick. **Out of the Shadows.** Minneapolis, MN: CompCare Publications, 1983.

Greenleaf, Jael. "Co-Alcoholics/Para-Alcoholics: Who's Who and What's the Difference?" **Co-dependency, An Emerging Issue.** Pompano Beach, FL: Health Communications, 1984.

Kaufman, Gershen. **Shame: The Power of Caring.** Cambridge, MA: Schenkman Books, 1980.

Kritsberg, Wayne. **The ACoA Syndrome.** Pompano Beach, FL: Health Communications, 1985.

Lerner, Rokelle. **Daily Affirmations.** Pompano Beach, FL: Health Communications, 1985.

Smith, Ann. **Grandchildren of Alcoholics.** Pompano Beach, FL: Health Communications, 1988.

Wegscheider-Cruse, Sharon. **Another Chance: Hope and Health for the Alcoholic Family.** Palo Alto, CA: Science & Behavior Books, 1981.

Woititz, Janet. **Adult Children of Alcoholics.** Pompano Beach, FL: Health Communications, 1983.

The Baby Boom

Jones, Landon Y. **Great Expectations: America and the Baby Boom Generation.** New York: Ballantine Books, 1980.

Levinson, Daniel. **The Seasons of a Man's Life.** New York: Alfred A. Knopf, 1978.

Student Assistance Programs

Buchannan, Jean. **Epidemic In Retreat.** Cleveland, OH: Glenbeigh Institute, 1984.

Crowley, James. **Alliance For Change.** Minneapolis, MN: Community Intervention, 1984.

Haiback, Frank; McCullough, Peggy, and Taylor, Nancy in Barr, Frank, and Terbanc, Barbara (eds.). **Project CARE Model.** Project CARE, 390 Front Street, Berea, OH 44017, 1986.

Books from . . .
Health Communications

AFTER THE TEARS: Reclaiming The Personal Losses of Childhood
Jane Middelton-Moz and Lorie Dwinnel
Your lost childhood must be grieved in order for you to recapture your
self-worth and enjoyment of life. This book will show you how.
ISBN 0-932194-36-2 $7.95

HEALING YOUR SEXUAL SELF
Janet Woititz
How can you break through the aftermath of sexual abuse and enter into
healthy relationships? Survivors are shown how to recognize the problem
and deal effectively with it.
ISBN 1-55874-018-X $7.95

RECOVERY FROM RESCUING
Jacqueline Castine
Effective psychological and spiritual principles teach you when to take
charge, when to let go, and how to break the cycle of guilt and fear that
keeps you in the responsibility trap. Mind-altering ideas and exercises will
guide you to a more carefree life.
ISBN 1-55874-016-3 $7.95

ADDICTIVE RELATIONSHIPS: Reclaiming Your Boundaries
Joy Miller
We have given ourselves away to spouse, lover, children, friends or
parents. By examining where we are, where we want to go and how to get
there, we can reclaim our personal boundaries and the true love of
ourselves.
ISBN 1-55874-003-1 $7.95

RECOVERY FROM CO-DEPENDENCY:
It's Never Too Late To Reclaim Your Childhood
Laurie Weiss, Jonathan B. Weiss
Having been brought up with life-repressing decisions, the adult child
recognizes something isn't working. This book shows how to change
decisions and live differently and fully.
ISBN 0-932194-85-0 $9.95

SHIPPING/HANDLING: All orders shipped UPS unless weight exceeds 200 lbs., special routing is requested, or
delivery territory is outside continental U.S. Orders outside United States shipped either Air Parcel Post or Surface
Parcel Post. Shipping and handling charges apply to all orders shipped whether UPS, Book Rate, Library Rate, Air
or Surface Parcel Post or Common Carrier and will be charged as follows. Orders less than $25.00 in value add
$2.00 minimum. Orders from $25.00 to $50.00 in value (after discount) add $2.50 minimum. Orders greater than
$50.00 in value (after discount) add 6% of value. Orders greater than $25.00 outside United States add 15% of
value. We are not responsible for loss or damage unless material is shipped UPS. Allow 3-5 weeks after receipt of
order for delivery. Prices are subject to change without prior notice.

Enterprise Center, 3201 S.W. 15th Street,
Deerfield Beach, FL 33442
1-800-851-9100

Health
Communications, Inc.

Other Books By . . .
Health Communications, Inc.

ADULT CHILDREN OF ALCOHOLICS
Janet Woititz
Over a year on *The New York Times* Best-Seller list, this book is the primer on Adult Children of Alcoholics.
ISBN 0-932194-15-X   **$6.95**

STRUGGLE FOR INTIMACY
Janet Woititz
Another best-seller, this book gives insightful advice on learning to love more fully.
ISBN 0-932194-25-7   **$6.95**

DAILY AFFIRMATIONS: For Adult Children of Alcoholics
Rokelle Lerner
These positive affirmations for every day of the year paint a mental picture of your life as you choose it to be.
ISBN 0-932194-27-3   **$6.95**

CHOICEMAKING: For Co-dependents, Adult Children and Spirituality Seekers — Sharon Wegscheider-Cruse
This useful book defines the problems and solves them in a positive way.
ISBN 0-932194-26-5   **$9.95**

LEARNING TO LOVE YOURSELF: Finding Your Self-Worth
Sharon Wegscheider-Cruse
"Self-worth is a choice, not a birthright", says the author as she shows us how we can choose positive self-esteem.
ISBN 0-932194-39-7   **$7.95**

BRADSHAW ON: THE FAMILY: A Revolutionary Way of Self-Discovery
John Bradshaw
The host of the nationally televised series of the same name shows us how families can be healed and individuals can realize full potential.
ISBN 0-932194-54-0   **$9.95**

HEALING THE CHILD WITHIN:
Discovery and Recovery for Adult Children of Dysfunctional Families
Charles Whitfield
Dr. Whitfield defines, describes and discovers how we can reach our Child Within to heal and nurture our woundedness.
ISBN 0-932194-40-0   **$8.95**

Enterprise Center, 3201 S.W. 15th Street,
Deerfield Beach, FL 33442
1-800-851-9100

Health Communications, Inc.

New Books . . .
from Health Communications

Helpful 12-Step Books from . . .
Health Communications

HEALING A BROKEN HEART:
12 Steps of Recovery for Adult Children
Kathleen W.
This useful 12-Step book is presently the number one resource for all
Adult Children support groups.
ISBN 0-932194-65-6   **$7.95**

12 STEPS TO SELF-PARENTING For Adult Children
Philip Oliver-Diaz and Patricia A. O'Gorman
This gentle 12-Step guide takes the reader from pain to healing and self-
parenting, from anger to forgiveness, and from fear and despair to
recovery.
ISBN 0-932194-68-0   **$7.95**

THE 12-STEP STORY BOOKLETS
Mary M. McKee
Each beautifully illustrated booklet deals with a step, using a story from
nature in parable form. The 12 booklets (one for each step) lead us to a
better understanding of ourselves and our recovery.
ISBN 1-55874-002-3   **$8.95**

WITH GENTLENESS, HUMOR AND LOVE:
A 12-Step Guide for Adult Children in Recovery
Kathleen W. and Jewell E.
Focusing on adult child issues such as reparenting the inner child, self-
esteem, intimacy and feelings, this well-organized workbook teaches
techniques and tools for the 12-step recovery programs.
ISBN 0-932194-77-X   **$7.95**

GIFTS FOR PERSONAL GROWTH & RECOVERY
Wayne Kritsberg
A goldmine of positive techniques for recovery (affirmations, journal
writing, visualizations, guided meditations, etc.), this book is indispens-
able for those seeking personal growth.
ISBN 0-932194-60-5   **$6.95**

Enterprise Center, 3201 S.W. 15th Street,
Deerfield Beach, FL 33442
1-800-851-9100

**Health
Communications, Inc.**

Daily Affirmation Books from . . .
Health Communications

GENTLE REMINDERS FOR CO-DEPENDENTS: Daily Affirmations
Mitzi Chandler
With insight and humor, Mitzi Chandler takes the co-dependent and the
adult child through the year. Gentle Reminders is for those in recovery
who seek to enjoy the miracle each day brings.
ISBN 1-55874-020-1 $6.95

TIME FOR JOY: Daily Affirmations
Ruth Fishel
With quotations, thoughts and healing energizing affirmations these daily
messages address the fears and imperfections of being human, guiding us
through self-acceptance to a tangible peace and the place within where
there is time for joy.
ISBN 0-932194-82-6 $6.95

CRY HOPE: Positive Affirmations For Healthy Living
Jan Veltman
This book gives positive daily affirmations for seekers and those in
recovery. Everyday is a new adventure, and change is a challenge.
ISBN 0-932194-74-5 $6.95

SAY YES TO LIFE: Daily Affirmations For Recovery
Father Leo Booth
These meditations take you through the year day by day with Father Leo
Booth, looking for answers and sometimes discovering that there are
none. Father Leo tells us, "For the recovering compulsive person God is
too important to miss — may you find Him now."
IBN 0-932194-46-X $6.95

DAILY AFFIRMATIONS: For Adult Children of Alcoholics
Rokelle Lerner
Affirmations are a way to discover personal awareness, growth and
spiritual potential, and self-regard. Reading this book gives us an
opportunity to nurture ourselves, learn who we are and what we want to
become.
ISBN 0-932194-47-3
(Little Red Book) $6.95
(New Cover Edition) $6.95

Enterprise Center, 3201 S.W. 15th Street,
Deerfield Beach, FL 33442
1-800-851-9100